Development of

AUDIOLINGUISTIC SKILLS
IN CHILDREN

Development of

AUDIOLINGUISTIC SKILLS
IN CHILDREN

By
MERLIN J. MECHAM, Ph.D.
Director, Speech Pathology & Audiology
University of Utah
Salt Lake City, Utah

WARREN H. GREEN, INC.
St. Louis, Missouri, U.S.A.

Published and distributed by

WARREN H. GREEN, INC.
10 South Brentwood Blvd.
St. Louis, Missouri 63105, U.S.A.

© *1969 by WARREN H. GREEN, INC.*

Library of Congress Catalog Card No. 67-26014

Printed in the United States of America
4-A

162

PREFACE

For the past decade or so, there has been a rapidly growing interest within many academic fields and disciplines concerning linguistic development in children. The field of speech pathology and audiology is especially interested in developmental audiolinguistic (oral-aural language) behavior and audiolinguistic disorders. Since present theories stress the importance of the first five years of life for proper language development, this period in the life of the child has become of special interest.

Scientific investigations concerning language development are in a very preliminary stage. In this book, much of what is presented is therefore hypothetical. This is not bad because hypothetical ideas should be vulnerable to scientific verification. When we realize that even in the carefully controlled studies of the functions of the sensory end-organs all variables cannot be controlled, as pointed out by Dr. Georg von Bekesy in his classical *Sensory Inhibition* (Princeton University Press, 1967), we can well guess the problems involved in the scientific study of complex language behavior. There *are* some semi-hard generalizations available about language development and these serve as the bases undergirding the frames of reference presented here.

A great number of professional persons (speech therapists, head-start teachers, etc.) throughout the country are trying to stimulate and facilitate more adequate language development in children as a major effort. Some of them have very little background knowledge concerning development of audiolinguistic skills in children, and it is to these persons that the present volume is directed. Information which the author considers to be a minimal requisite for those trying to facilitate language development is presented, and ways in which this information can be utilized in practice are suggested. Sections are of necessity brief and therefore often abstract; but the author has tried to present adequate references for more extended study in each instance.

Not many notions herein are original. They have been gleaned from many fields as well as from the author's own clinical experiences. I am indebted to my colleagues and students for their stimulation and criticisms. To the Remedial Center for Communication Disorders (Nebo, Utah, School District), I owe a special thanks for demonstrating clearly some of the pressing problems which exist in the public schools. I wish to express my gratitude especially to my wife Neva for her encouragement and for her assistance in proofing; to Marjorie Jacobson for typing and re-typing the manuscript; and to Laurence Hilton for assisting with the illustrations. To various publishers, wherever I have not given due credit, my apologies; where I have given adequate documentation, my thanks for your kindness.

M.J.M.

CONTENTS

Page

PREFACE v

Chapter

One – INTRODUCTION 2
A Developmental Phenomena–Psycholinguistic Model–
Linguistic Structure–Summary and Perspective

Two – INTRINSIC ORGANISMIC VARIABLES AFFECTING
LANGUAGE BEHAVIOR 12
Introduction–Motor Development–Perceptual and
Cognitive Development–Age and Sensitivity–Summary

Three – EXTRINSIC VARIABLES AFFECTING LANGUAGE BEHAVIOR 22
Early Sensory Stimulation–Dependency or Attachment–
Spatial Exploration–Experience–Practice and Mimicry–
Creativity and Independence–Summary

Four – MEASUREMENT OF AUDIOLINGUISTIC AND CLOSELY
RELATED SKILLS 32
Evaluation of Perceptual Functions Related to Language
Competence–Ability to Form Concepts–Ability to
Abstract–Auditory Identification–Auditory Discrimina-
tion–Auditory Memory–Oral Stereognosis–The Audio-
linguistic Ladder–Analysis of Quality of Linguistic
Structure–Linguistic Competence–Linguistic Performance–
Summary

Five – FACILITATION OF AUDIOLINGUISTIC SKILLS IN
LANGUAGE DELAYED CHILDREN 44
Introduction–Strengthening Organismic Variables–
Auditory Perception–Oral Stereognosis–Strengthening
an Eliciting Environment–Providing Real or Contrived
Experiences–Encouraging Interaction Between Concept
and Language Organization–Increasing Motivation by
Strengthening Stimulus Variables–Summary

Appendix 68
Outline of the Main Elements of Operant Conditioning

Author Index 71
Index 73

Development of

AUDIOLINGUISTIC SKILLS
IN CHILDREN

Chapter One

INTRODUCTION

Our observations of the speaking behavior of others is made possible primarily through watching and listening. We watch the face and particularly the mouth of the speaker and listen to approximately 800 phonemes per minute being formulated by constantly changing patterns of over a hundred muscles acting together for various phonemes (approximately 14 phoneme patterns per second).

Man has been listening and speaking for well nigh a million years. Coincidentally, the unfolding and developmental emergence of oral language in the young child under normal conditions seems to be a rather spontaneous and biologically predisposed function (Lenneberg, 1967). Reading and writing, on the other hand, are relatively new forms of language function: not many years ago, reading and writing was the privilege of only a certain few, and at least half of the present population of the world are illiterate (Moulton, 1966). It is extremely handicapping in any culture, no matter how primitive, not to be able to listen and speak with some degree of proficiency. It is possible, however, in almost any culture, to get by with a fair degree of independence without knowing how to read and write. These latter skills are very convenient and are in vogue in education. But they are not absolutely essential to normal social function. For this reason, listening and speaking are referred to as the basic modes of language, and reading and writing are referred to as supplementary language skills. It is not intended here to reduce reading and writing to a level of secondary importance, but merely to stress the fact that these two forms of language are psychologically and biologically two rather distinct and different systems. *Throughout the present manual, when we refer to verbal language, we will be referring to the more basic audiolinguistic functions of listening and speaking.*

Interest in quantitative measures of linguistic development has not been lessening in the past few years; on the contrary, it seems to have increased considerably along with the increased public demand for personal evaluative services. There has also been an increased interest in differential evaluation utilizing qualitative measures in semantic and syntactic function (McNeill, 1966).

A DEVELOPMENTAL PHENOMENON

There is substantial evidence that language relationships demonstrate a highly predictable maturational or developmental dimension. Lenneberg (1964) has aptly stated that, even though we cannot find any historical connection between language families, the onset of speech and language is a very regular phenomena, "appearing at a certain time in the child's physical development and following a fixed sequence of events" (p. 66). Recognizable behavioral milestones emerge at predictable ages universally. Kephart (1968, p. 13) has stressed the importance of developmental experiences for the child during the early years.

> Hierarchical relationships in learning exist on the readiness level as well as on the academic level. Certain readiness skills are dependent upon each other just as certain academic skills are dependent upon each other. These readiness skills are in part the result of maturation but they are in part the result of learning. If the necessary learning experiences in the readiness stage are not presented, the hierarchy of readiness skills may be upset with resulting confusion at the higher levels.

According to Kephart (1968), a child learns through the process of generalizing the information which comes from sensory data which are acquired through the interaction of the child with his environment. This generalization comes about by the child's learning a repertoire of *variations* of response which are effective in achieving approximately the same goal. It also comes by learning to *integrate* various forms in which information is presented to the child (i.e., learning to utilize redundancies). This process of learning comes through a great variety of experiences, successfully encountered through *varied* responses and sensory *integration* of differing modes of incoming information.

PSYCHOLINGUISTIC MODEL

In addition to language demonstrating predictable developmental dimensions in time with the organism interacting with his environment, language events can be classified generally into four symbolic behavioral processes: (1) semantic encoding; (2) grammatical encoding; (3) semantic decoding, and (4) grammatical decoding.* Brain damaged adults and children have been reported to have difficulties in each of these process areas (Taylor, 1966; Wepman, 1968). Succinct examples of these four processes in normal language behavior have been given by Moulton (1966, pp. 24-42).

> *Semantic encoding.* We shall assume, first of all, that A has some sort of 'idea' or 'thought' or 'meaning' that he wants to communicate to B .... The task that now faces A is: How can he get this idea into such a shape that it can be communicated in the language he is using? Let us suppose ... that he wants to describe the color of some object. We all know that, within the color spectrum, there is an infinite variety of shades. And yet, if A is speaking English, the spectrum has not an infinite number of colors but only six [or seven] ... It has many more; but only these six (or seven) are basic ....
>
> If, as a speaker of English, A wants to describe the color of some object, he must first shape his idea so that it will fit into the semantic system of English color terms. Since this is like putting a message into the proper shape to fit the code in which it is to be sent, we can call the process 'semantic encoding.' In effect, *every* message first has to undergo semantic encoding before it can be sent.

.   .   .   .

---

*Phonological encoding and decoding are also important aspects of the behavior of language, but are not treated here since they are usually given comprehensive treatment in most writings in the field of communication disorders.

Grammatical encoding. Once speaker A has found the proper semantic units to express his thought, he must next arrange them in the particular way that his language requires. The scheme by which this arranging is done in a language is called the 'grammar' of the language' we may, therefore, refer to this stage of the speech event as that of 'grammatical encoding.' For example, if A's language is English, and if he wants to get across the idea of 'dog,' 'man,' and 'bite'—with the dog and not the man doing the biting—he has to encode it in the order *dog bites man*; the order *man bites dog* gives quite a different message.

.   .   .   .

Semantic decoding. Suppose ... We received a message which we tentatively decode as: 'I'll senate by air mail' . . . . The item *senate* is marked as 'noun,' whereas the code tells us that, in 'I'll X by Y,' the X must be a verb . . . . A quick check in the semantic code, however, reveals that 'to senate by mail' just doesn't make sense . . . . [Past experience will tell us that we 'send' things by mail and that in American English we] drop the final /d/ and /n/ [thus we soon come to the conclusion that what the speaker intended to say was 'I will send it by mail.' Semantic decoding then involves the task of recognizing enough bits of information in the entire code to enable him to match the code with a concept which he has previously learned.]

.   .   .   .

Grammatical decoding. We assume at this stage that the message, neatly broken up into a sequence of phonemes, is being passed along from the phonological to the grammatical code. Hearer B's task is now one of grouping these phonemes into grammatical units of various sizes: morphemes, words, phrases, clauses, sentences—as well as larger structures involving sequence of sentences. Somehow he must take the message as it arrives, match it against his own built-in grammatical code (which must be essentially the same as A's), and decode it in this way.

An understanding of the expected emergences (or milestones) of language and their relation to time in early development lays some *general* guidelines for quantitative evaluations of language development. The present writer, in collaboration with two other audiolinguists, has attempted to look at some developmental schedules of language patterns which have appeared historically in

TABLE I
DEVELOPMENTAL LANGUAGE ITEMS* CLASSIFIED ACCORDING TO LANGUAGE PROCESSES

Semantic Decoding	Norm Age	Norm N	Semantic Encoding	Norm Age	Norm N
Responds to name and 'no-no'	0-9	496	Marks with pencil or crayon	1-4	883
Recognizes names of objects	1-6	496	Names common pictures	2-2	496
Recognizes names of 3 body parts	1-7	3,187	Names common pictures	2-3	496
Identifies names of pictures	1-10	496	Names a color	2-9	496
Identifies action in pictures	2-8	496	Names common pictures	3-5	496
Receptive vocabulary	2-11	4,285	Names primary colors	4-1	496
Receptive vocabulary	5-10	4,285	Draws with pencil or crayon	5-0	883
Reads words in pre-primer	6-6	393	Prints simple words	5-6	883
Receptive vocabulary	7-1	4,285	Names penny, nickle, dime	6-1	393
Receptive vocabulary	9-11	4,285	Names quarter, ½ dol., dol.	7-3	393
Receptive vocabulary	12-7	4,285	Can rhyme words	9-0	3,187
Receptive vocabulary	15-4	4,285			

Sequential Decoding	Norm Age	Norm N	Sequential Encoding	Norm Age	Norm N
Responds to simple instructions	1-1	883	Word combinations of two or more	2-0	496
Can repeat two digits	2-5	3,187	Says full name	3-3	496
Responds to simple commands	2-6	3,187	Says a nursery rhyme	3-8	496
Can repeat three digits	3-1	3,187	Copies a cross	3-10	3,187
Can repeat four digits	4-4	3,187	Copies a square	5-3	3,187
Carries out three commissions	4-7	3,187	Writes numbers to thirties	6-3	393
Can repeat 12 syll. sentence	4-9	3,187	Tells a familiar story	6-5	393
Can repeat five digits	7-7	3,187	Counts by ones to fifty	6-8	393
Can repeat 16 syll. sentence	8-3	3,187	Copies a diamond	6-11	3,187
Can repeat four digits reversed	9-5	3,187	Names the days of the week	7-11	3,187
Can repeat six digits	10-5	3,187	Writes cursively	8-8	883
Can repeat 20 syll. sentence	10-11	3,187			
Can repeat five digits reversed	12-0	3,187			
Can repeat five one-syll. words	13-5	3,187			
Can repeat difficult sentence	14-6	3,187			
Follows directional sequences	16-0	3,187			

*Taken from the *Utah Test of Language Development (1967 Edition)*.

standardized tests, to arrange then segmentally according to age progression, and to classify these in accordance with the four basic symbolic processes of language function, i.e., semantic decoding, semantic encoding, grammatical decoding, and grammatical encoding.

Table 1 shows a classification distribution of various developmental items taken from several standardized test sources. The table also lists the age calibrations of the items and the size of the population samples on which the items have been standardized. This listing includes all of the items recently collected and calibrated into the Utah Test of Language Development (Mecham *et al.,* 1967). From this table, it can be seen that these language items not only distribute fairly evenly among the four processes of language, but also represent a fairly uniform age progression under each category. The milestones of development which these items represent are seen to emerge quickly and distinctly and can be used as landmarks of the child's maturational levels of language behavior.

LINGUISTIC STRUCTURE

Better understanding of *grammatical structure* provides more specific insight by which one can judge the structural quality of the child's audiolinguistic skills. Following is a brief and simplified description of some of the important grammatical structures of language:

a. The *word* is the smallest meaningful unit of grammar. Words may be grouped into two general classes, i.e., (1) open class in which an infinite number of words can be added to the class, and (2) closed class in which the number of words are finite and cannot be increased. Functional groupings of words within classes are called *parts.* Those parts falling under the open class (content words) are generally called *nouns, verbs, adjectives,* and *adverbs* (in-ly), in accordance with their **semantic** reference to *things, actions,* and *variability.* Those parts falling under the closed class (function*

---

*These words are much more difficult to classify than are the content words.

words) are generally called *pronouns, auxiliary verbs, articles* or *determiners, prepositions, coordinating conjunctions, subordinating conjunctions, adverbs* (generally not in-ly), *question* words (e.g., why), and *substitutes* (e.g., then) in accordance with their **grammatical** function of relating words to other words within a sentence. (Moulton, 1966, pp. 87-90)

b. The *sentence* is the smallest functional unit of language. It is normally comprised of two basic slots, i.e., *noun* (subject) and *verb* (predicate). The two slots in the basic sentence can be either expanded from a word to two or more words or phrases, or vice-versa, they can by contracted.

Various forms of the *basic* sentence can be generated, mainly, the *elliptical* sentence (e.g., use of "eight tonight" rather than, "I'll be there at eight o'clock tonight."), the *compound* sentence (i.e., two potential full sentences combined into one), and the *complex* sentence (i.e., imbedding one sentence inside another). (Moulton, 1966, pp. 67-76)

c. *Transformations* are phrase or sentence structures which *deviate from* the so-called *basic* sentence structure; they make it possible for differing sentence arrangements to have the same meanings. Transformations are derived from the basic sentence structure and include the following most common forms: (1) order transformations in which the basic order is changed as in "Give the money to me;" (2) transformation of full forms into substitute forms as in the case where "men, women, and children" are designated by the substitute word "they"; (3) transformation of a positive statement into a negative as in the case where "I have money" is transformed to "I have no money"; (4) transformation of a statement into a question by use of inflectional change or by use of some part of a closed class such as *who, whose,* or *where;* (5) transformation of a statement to a command; (6) transformation of an active statement to a passive statement; (7) coordinate transformations where two sentences are alike in every way except that a particular slot is represented in the one by X and in the other by Y, and they can be transformationally combined by changing the slot in question to "X and Y" —an example of this is the sentence, "This machine *washes* and *dries* clothes"; (8) transformation of a statement into a nominal clause (i.e., into a clause which fills a *noun phrase* slot; e.g., "It is true that the world is round"); (9) transformation of a statement into an adjectival clause (i.e., a clause that modifies a *noun phrase*; e.g., "we saw the car he rides in"); (10) transformation of a statement into an adverbial clause, e.g., "We arrived when it was too late." There are many more examples of transformations which could be discussed, but these give a fair idea of the complexity of language structure. (Moulton, 1966, pp. 77-86)

The above descriptions of language structure are of necessity very brief and sketchy. For much greater detail on the general qualitative properties of language, the reader is encouraged to consult current standard textbooks in linguistics (Gleason, 1965; Jacobs and Rosenbaum, 1968; etc.).

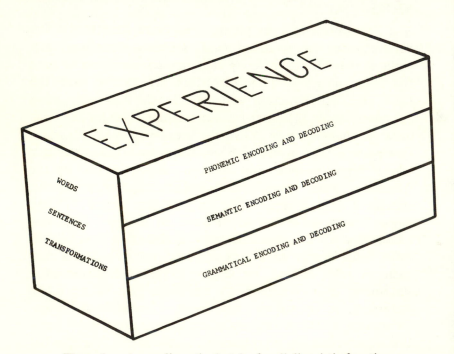

Figure 1.   A paradigmatic sketch of audiolinguistic function.

SUMMARY AND PERSPECTIVE

The present chapter has introduced concepts regarding both language *behavior* and *structure.* Figure 1 illustrates a model which has been set forth in this chapter.

Chapters two and three take a close look at the organismic and environmental variables which seem to have an important influence upon audiolinguistic development; chapter four describes some current trends in the evaluation and measurement of audiolinguistic and closely related skills in children; and chapter five gives a rather detailed discussion of approaches which may be used to facilitate more normal development of audiolinguistic skills among language delayed children.

REFERENCES

GLEASON, H. A., Jr.: *Linguistics and English Grammar.* New York, Holt, Rinehart and Winston, 1965.

JACOBS, R. A., and ROSENBAUM, P. S.: *English Transformational Grammar.* Waltham, Mass., Blaisdell Publishing Co., 1968.

KEPHART, N. C.: *Learning Disability: An Educational Adventure.* West Lafayette, Ind., Kappa Delta Pi Press, 1968.

LENNEBERG, E. H.: *New Directions in the Study of Language.* Cambridge,. The M.I.T. Press, 1964.

McNEILL, D.: Developmental psycholinguistics. In SMITH, F., and MILLER, G.A.: *The Genesis of Language.* Cambridge, The M.I.T. Press, 1966.

MECHAM, M. J., JEX, J. L., and JONES, J. D.: *Utah Test of Language Development.* Salt Lake City (P.O. Box 11012), Communication Research Associates, 1967.

MILLER, W., and ERVIN, S.: The development of grammer in child language. In BELLUGI, E., and BROWN, R.: *The Acquisition of Language.* Monograph of the Society for Research in Child Development, *29*:9-35, 1964.

MOULTON, W. G.: *A Linguistic Guide to Language Learning.* New York., Modern Language Association, 1966.

TAYLOR, M.: Paper given at the Short Course in Language Disorders. Houston Hearing and Speech Center, Houston, Texas, 1966.

WEPMAN, J.: Aphasia: diagnostic description and therapy. *Hearing and Speech News, 36:1:*3-5, 22-26, 1968.

Chapter Two

INTRINSIC ORGANISMIC VARIABLES
AFFECTING LANGUAGE BEHAVIOR

INTRODUCTION

There are various motor and perceptual systems, the proper development of which are felt to be prerequisite to the kind of intricate control necessary for speech movements, language concepts, storage, and sequencing. Clinical experience has demonstrated that there is a very high degree of coincidence between deficits in the perceptual-motor systems and problems of communication. This observation is strengthened through the developmental neurobehavioral philosophy, the basic assumptions of which are: (1) That the higher mental functions are founded upon basic systems at various brain levels which, although separate systems, essentially relate to each other in some fashion during the language process (Ayres, 1967; Luria, 1966); and (2) that neurobehavioral patterns appear normally during "readiness" or "sensitivity" periods, at certain times during the child's life and unfold in an orderly manner (Lenneberg, 1967; Gesell, 1941).

Although it is perhaps artificial to think of the motor and perceptual skills as separate entities or developments, for purposes of academic understanding it is easier to treat them separately.

MOTOR DEVELOPMENT

Among the motor mechanisms which are observable developmentally, and whose deficits may interfere with developmental emergence of proper receptive and expressive language skills, are the postural and equilibrium systems, bilateral sychrony and orientation, and oral-cephalic reflexes. These will be discussed briefly in that order

Postural and Equilibrium Systems. These systems are primarily a function of brain centers below the level of the cortex, but depend upon a highly integrated cerebrum for their inhibition and selective control. They include the selective tonicity reflexes,* the righting reflexes,* and equilibrium reactions.

The selective tonicity reflexes include the tonic neck reflexes, the tonic labyrinthine reflexes, the Landou reflex, and the Moro reflex.

Tonic neck reflexes (TNR) consist of both symmetric and asymmetric reflexes. In the symmetric TNR, extensor tonus is increased in the arms and flexor tonus in the legs when the head is turned upward; when the head is turned downward these tonic relationships are reversed. In the asymmetric TNR, the rotation of the head laterally increases the extensor tonus in the extremities on the side of the body toward which the face is turned and increases the flexor tonus in the limbs on the opposite side of the body. The reflexes are generally present at birth and are inhibited in the waking state after about sixteen weeks.

Tonic labyrinthine reflexes (TLR) increases general extensor tonus when the body is supine and increases the general flexor tonus when the body is prone. It makes its appearance at one or two months and is inhibited before twelve months.

The Landou reflex tends to facilitate extensor tonus in the entire body when projected by the abdomen into the air. It remains with an individual most of his life and provides protection from falls through extension of the extremities.

The Moro reflex or "startle" consists of a sudden extension and then abduction of the upper trunk and extremities in reaction to an unexpected stimulus. It is present at birth and is strong during the first three months of life. It persists in some form throughout life.

---

*Ages expressed for these reflexes are those noted by Crickmay (1966) and Mysak (1968).

The **righting reflexes** enable the child to turn over from supine to the side and prone positions (Crickmay, 1966). They also help the child get into crawling and sitting positions. Although reflexive at first, these activities soon become volitional. The *neck righting reflex* tends to keep the upper trunk and head in a perpendicular relationship, while the *body righting reflex* tends to bring the lower trunk and extremities in line with the upper trunk and extremities. These reflexes seem to be most useful during the first five years of life. The *labyrinthine righting reflex* tends to keep the head oriented in a normal position in space, i.e., a position usually assumed in the vertical postural position. It appears at two to four months and is present throughout life. The *optic righting reflex* tends to supplement the labyrinthine righting reflex in maintaining a normal position of the head in space. This reflex appears at about four weeks and is present throughout life. The *equilibrium reactions* seem to play a major role in securing adequate coordination and balance for walking, running, jumping, climbing, etc., i.e., they assist the biped in coping with gravity during ambulation. (For a rather detailed description of these, see Mysak, 1968.)

Bilateral Sychrony and Orientation. Since unilateralization is unique to the human species as is language function, and since laterality seems to be closely related to language development, it seems logical that strong dexterity and bilateral synchrony are desirable goals for the language delayed child. Certainly, at the age when the child begins to dress himself, he must develop an orientation of body parts and directionality; he must know different parts of the body, be conscious of laterality and know the relationships between clothing and parts of his own body.

Oroneuromotor Behavior. The "speech related" reflexes (Mysak, 1968) seem to be vegetative in nature and tend to enable the young mammal infant to hunt for and find the food given off by the parent. These consist of the *facial response* (pouting protrusion of lips upon tapping around lips); *rooting reactions* (movement of face toward side of tactile stimulus around lips and month); *biting reflex* (biting action upon placing stimulus object between teeth or gums); *suckling reflex* (forward, upward, and backward movement of tongue upon touching stimulus to teeth, tongue, gums or hand palate); *chewing reflex* (chewing movements resulting from placing stimulation object between teeth).

The basic reflexes and coordinations described above tend to play a major role in the early development of motor behavior; and then most reflexes tend to become minimally observable or obscure as various intentional or propositional motor behaviors develop. Their disappearance is felt to be brought about by cerebral inhibition. If the inhibiting functions of the cerebrum are weakened, the *reflexes* may be abnormally present to varying degrees long after they are supposed to disappear and may interfere with finer and more variable voluntary behavior. Or, on the other hand, selective impairment or some of these reflexes or coordinating mechanisms may prevent the development of adequate volitional motor patterns later. Such deficits may not be apparent in a minimally brain-injured child except when he is in a highly propositional act, is under undue emotional stress, or has to perform complex and intricate movements.

Some common intentional or operant motor skills which we see emerge at a later time in the developing child include ambulatory coordination, object manipulation (such as is found in dressing, etc.) object receipt and/or propulsion (such as is found in various sports), movement synchrony and rhythm (Kephart, 1966); and various coordinated patterns found in breathing, phonating, and articulating during the speaking process.

PERCEPTUAL AND COGNITIVE DEVELOPMENT

Since *basic* language, i.e., listening and speaking, depend upon normal sensory and perceptual functions in the auditory and haptic-kinesthetic channels, a great deal of emphasis is given to the evaluation and training of these two functions.

There are many perceptual and cognitive functions which have been described and classified in the literature. Some of the more important ones whose deficits are likely to interfere with development of proper receptive and expressive communication skills are: (1) detection and recognition; (2) discrimination and rejection; (3) stimulus recall and scanning, and (4) categorization and abstraction. Each of these will be discussed briefly.

Detection and Recognition. Detection, or just noticeable awareness, is dependent upon sensitivity of the end organ as well as ability to recognize a stimulus, that is, it is harder to detect an unknown signal than it is to detect a signal that is known (Galanter, 1966, p. 123). Once the stimulus is detected beyond doubt, the task is to decide which of the various meaningful alternative patterns, in the experience repertoire of the person, it happens to be (recognition). The strength of the recognition task is determined by the number of possible similar alternatives in the experience repertoire of the individual which could be confused with the pattern; the skill level in recognition is the likelihood that one will correctly identify the pattern being observed; that is, what percentage of the time does one accurately identify the pattern out of say, one hundred times? The skill is dependent upon experience, detection threshold, discriminating ability, incentive, expectation, etc. (Galanter, 1966).

Accurate recognition of stimuli is affected by one's systematic orientation of relationship between the figure and ground variables. The more random and less systematic the background, the easier it is to conjure up a cognition of the figure as distinguished from the background. Conversely, the more systematic the background and the more similar its organization is to the organization of the figure, the more difficult it becomes to recognize the figure on such ground. In addition to figure-ground relationships, identification also depends heavily upon contextual clues (Lieberman, 1967).

Discrimination and Rejection. Discrimination is the ability to perceive a change in some variable or pattern or a difference between two stimuli. Just noticeable differences (jnds) are a function not only of the central nervous system but also seem to be influenced by the sense modality involved and organismic fluctuations within the modality. Rejection of an undesirable pattern is dependent upon discrimination ability as well as maturation and learning.

Since all speech sounds are made differently each time that they are made, all "sounds" should theoretically sound differently. The probability of reacting to the "s" sound as if it were a good "s" is greatest nearest the normal production area. If we progressively move our tongue forward and vary further from the average acoustical characteristics on each repetition of the "s" sound, the probability progressively decreases in terms of our reacting to it as being the same or as being a good "s." If, on the other hand, we move the tongue progressively back away from the median position for an "s" sound, we again increase variance from normal acoustical characteristics and decrease the probability that it will be reacted to as the same or as a good "s" sound. Figure 2 shows a hypothetical distribution of probability that a production will be identified as a good phoneme as a function of accuracy of motor and acoustical production.

By definition, the normal generalization region is Q2 + Q3, that is, we are more prone to react to the phoneme in this region as being "good" than in Q1 and Q4. Sharpening the discrimination ability in respect to differentiating a *good* from a *poor* phoneme would involve a process of obtaining smaller quartiles, that is, training the child to be able to reject the phoneme more quickly as the aritculatory characteristics change, i.e., as the tongue is moved forward or backward from the median tongue position.

Needless to say, one whose auditory discrimination powers are not very sharp will have difficulty differentiating between many

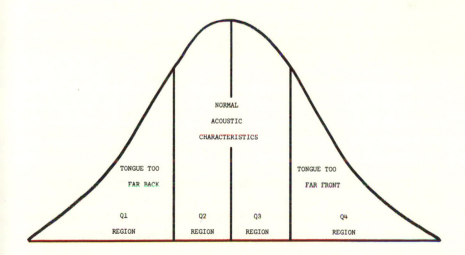

Figure 2.   Probability of reacting to phoneme as a good one.

sounds or many words which are rather similar, e.g., voiceless sibilants, voiced plosives, *nine* versus *mine*, etc. The relationship between auditory discrimination and *language acquisition* is vague if it exists at all. It is probably most important in the process of monitoring of self with model in articulation maturation.

Stimulus Recall and Scanning. Storage or memory plays at least two parts in the encoding and decoding of language. *First,* the phonemes and words which are being emitted or listened to must be tentatively stored long enough to stop them in time so to speak so that the listener or speaker can scan back and forth over them to be sure that they are in proper sequence or to check the sequence in which they are arranged. For example, in listening to the phrase, "suit yourself," the phonetic arrangement of what sounds like *suture* is stored long enough to check it with the other elements of the sentence. Secondly, we check this total arrangement with rules and past patterns which we have stored over a rather long term basis to see how to *read* meaning into what we have heard (Moulton, 1966). This would suggest that both *short term memory* and *long term memory* or storage is involved, that is, memory of the pattern we have just heard (short term) and memory of rules and past patterns which we have experienced. Another example refers to just the reverse in the encoding process. The fact that we can alter our construction in the middle of the utterance would suggest that we store what we have said long enough to be able to match it up with a newly construed ending; or sometimes after completing a sentence such as, "He is a very comprehensive person," we may go on and say, "Did I say comprehensive, I meant to say competent." Again, long term and short term memory play a role; one can remember what one just said and can also check it against earlier stored rules and patterns which one has experienced. If what we have said is not quite congruous, we can change it.

Categorizing and Abstracting. According to Lenneberg (1967), all higher animals have the ability to organize the sensory world through a categorizing process.* This process seems to involve the ability to react to things with some functional equivalence as a class of things, that is, to react to all of them in the same way. Lenneberg (1967) calls this propensity for responding to categories *concept formation*. We cluster things together in respect to a common criterion.

We discussed earlier the notion that words are used as labels for things and conceptual gestalts. (This is a major deviation in the human species from other species; no other species, as far as we know, can label its own concepts.) Thus, if labels are to be representative of concepts, they must be representative of categories. We therefore must not only be able to organize sensory data into concepts, we must be able to organize labels categorically to reflect the sensory data.

Abstracting is considered to be the process of leaving out details. In the categorizing process, the abstraction level of a category can be assessed in terms of the number of subcategories which fall under it. Thus, the concept of "boy" is less abstract (more concrete) than the concept of "people" because it contains less possible sub-classifications.

It is not difficult to see the importance of the skills in categorizing and abstracting in communication; the communication process traverses horizontally across categories and vertically through levels of abstraction with every single clause.

AGE AND SENSITIVITY

Sensory-perceptual-motor functions in the communication process seem to be greatly influenced by age and physical maturation. Lenneberg (1967) states that "language is not an arbitrarily adopted behavior, facilitated by accidentally fortunate anatomical arrangements in the oral cavity and larynx, but an activity which develops harmonously by necessary integration of neuronal and skeletal structures and by reciprocal adaptation of various physiological processes" (p. 175). Age limited emergence of behavior is common in all animals and is most drastically illustrated in what is called "imprinting" in many species. The

---

*Russian studies have shown that well directed and effective "orientation" reactions are essential to formation of conditioned reactions. There is little doubt that orientation reaction is a critical factor in learning and is impaired in most children with language-learning disabilities (Luria, 1963; Lynn, 1966; Mark and Hardy, 1958).

The relationship between orientation reaction and language acquisition is an important area for future study.

limiting factors postulated by Lenneberg in the case of language development are "cerebral immaturity on the one end and termination of a state of organizational plasticity linked with lateralization of function at the other end of the critical period" (p. 176).

The basic cerebral organization for language function seems to occur between ages two and twelve years, with a greatest focus of intensity of organization being around the third and fourth year (by age five lateralization of cerebral dominance becomes rather obvious). This period of plasticity for organizing is referred to as the "sensitivity" period for language acquisition. A rather impressive array of empirical as well as deductive evidence has been compiled to support this assumption (Lenneberg, 1967).

SUMMARY

The intrinsic variables most affecting language development are motor and perceptive skills which serve as the brick and mortar with which language is formed. Motor mechanisms which inhibit interference from early postural and consumatory reflexes and those which facilitate the child's being able to interact as normally as possible in manipulative activities and social sports are important targets in the training program. Perceptual skills which are necessary for achieving language competence and performance include perceptual recognition, discrimination and rejection, storing and scanning, categorizing and abstracting. Age is also an important variable in language acquisition, since sensitivity curves for language learning are functionally dependent upon age and physical maturation.

REFERENCES

AYRES, J.: Remedial procedures based on neurobehavioral constructs. In *Proceedings, 1967 International Convocation on Children and Young Adults with Learning Disabilities.* Home for Crippled Children, Pittsburg, Pa., 1967.

CRICKMAY, M. C.: *Speech Therapy and the Bobath Approach to Cerebral Palsy.* Springfield, Ill., Thomas, 1966.

GALANTER, E.: Contemporary psychophysics. In BROWN, R., *et al.: New Directions in Psychology I.* New York, Holt, Rinehart and Winston, Inc., 1962.

GESELL, A.: *Infant Development.* New York, Harper, 1952.

KEPHART, N. C.: The needs of teachers in specialized information on perception. In CRUICKSHANK, W. M. (Ed.): *The Teacher of Brain-injured Children.* New York, Syracuse University Press, 1966.

LENNEBERG, E. H.: *The Biological Basis of Language.* New York, Wiley, 1967.

LIEBERMAN, P.: *Intonation, Perception, and Language.* Cambridge, M.I.T. Press, 1967.

LURIA, A. R.: *The Mentally Retarded Child.* Oxford, Pergamon Press, 1963.

LURIA, A. R.: *Higher Cortical Functions in Man.* New York, Basic Books, 1966.

LYNN, R.: *Attention, Arousal and the Orientation Reaction.* Oxford, Pergamon Press, 1966.

MARK, H. J., and HARDY, W. G.: Orienting reflex disturbances in central auditory or language handicapped children. *JSHD, 23*:3:237-242, 1958.

MECHAM, M. J., BERKO, M. J., and BERKO, F. G.: *Communication Training in Childhood Brain Damage.* Springfield, Ill., Thomas, 1966.

MOULTON, W. G.: *A Linguistic Guide to Language Learning.* New York, Modern Language Association, 1966.

MYSAK, E. D.: *Neuroevolutional Approach to Cerebral Palsy and Speech.* New York: Columbia University Teachers College Press, 1968.

Chapter Three

EXTRINSIC VARIABLES AFFECTING
LANGUAGE BEHAVIOR

Audiolinguistic skills explode at ages two and three years, and basic language function is pretty well established by the age of five. The implications are that we must look to environmental variables which interact in the child's life prior to age five in any quest to determine environmental influences on language. Although we can, as yet, not do much more than speculate on which variables have the most influence and about ways in which language is affected, there are some important environmental relationships which warrant some careful attention in the study of language development in children. The present chapter is devoted to a treatment of some of these relationships.

EARLY SENSORY STIMULATION

Schiefelbusch (1967) discusses the early influence of sensory stimulation in the development of the child. He quoted a study which showed "that the conditioning of the infant vocalizations to social responses of an adult is possible as early as three months and that the social response of an adult can serve as a reinforcing stimulus" (p. 94).

Certain sensory cues seem to arouse attention in a very young infant. For instance, he will turn in the direction of a sound, his eyes will fixate more often on bright, shiny objects and will follow objects which are moving. The face of the human adult seems to arouse attention and pleasure reactions from the child. "It is apparent . . . that long before the infant begins to use speech or to respond actively to the speech material of adults around him, he is engaging in a kind of visual, social responsiveness which is stimulating to the child and which involves reciprocal exchanges with adults in his environment. Ultimately, these exchanges may be an important feature of his speech and language development" (Schiefelbusch, 1967, p. 95).

Apparently, the mother is the most important stimulator during the first few months of life—visually, auditorily, and through physical handling. The arousal and alertness created by the mother encourages him to exercise the use of his sensory and perceptual faculties (Schiefelbusch, 1967).

DEPENDENCY AND ATTACHMENT

Mussen (1967) talks about the importance of the development of dependency in the young infant; the mother's warmth, comfort, affection, fondling, stimulation, etc., seem to be so rewarding to the young infant that he develops a need for closeness to his mother which is independent of his physical needs. The development of attachment seems to be universal among all cultures. The mother apparently becomes a conditioned reinforcer, having been paired with food, warmth, and comfort. Conversely, if early interactions with the mother are paired with uncomfortable or aversive conditions such as being "neglected, inadequately nurtured, or cared for in harsh ways, handled roughly and held in tense, awkward positions," the parent may become a negative reinforcer (that is, behavior which avoids the parent is reinforcing) (Mussen, 1967, p. 65).

According to Erickson (1950), the "attachment" or "detachment" of a child may generalize to other persons. Erickson (1950) labels this appetitive or aversive gradient as *trust* or *distrust* respectively and believes that an extreme form of distrust results in schizophrenia. Children raised in institutions are generally less alert and more passive. They do not interact socially as intensely.

Eventually, when "trust" is developed in the child he can turn more and more away from his parent toward others through dependency generalization and eventually to himself for self-dependency. Without this "trust" a child may lack self-control, develop aggressiveness or symbiotic psychosis, or become distractable and hyperactive (Mussen, 1967).

Sloan (1968) has suggested that a child will do much of what he does in copy of the model with which he identifies or that he has observed being reinforced. Thus, a child may identify with a "model" and pattern much of his behavior after the model. Much of this "identification" results from reinforcement emanating from the nurturent and rewarding interactions between the model and the child.

Mussen (1967) reported a study which tested the hypothesis that girls of warm nurturent mothers were more prone to imitate the mother than girls whose mothers were considered cool and non-nurturent. There was a significant difference between the two groups in imitation of irrelevant (not task related) directions for completing a strange task, in favor of the nurturent mothers.

In respect to development of conscience and moral identification with parents, one outstanding study showed that maternal warmth and affection were positively related to strength of conscience and moral behavior in young children. "The highest level of conscience is most likely to be achieved by children whose mothers are warm, affectionate, and loving, but who make their love and support contingent upon the child's good behavior" (Mussen, 1967, p. 101.

Shaefer (1963) feels that attachment develops most readily when there is a condition of mutual influence between the parent and child, that is, where the parents responses are cued by the demands and behavior of the infant and where the child reciprocates in responding to the desires of the parent.

SPATIAL EXPLORATION

At one and one-half, a child experiences more distance between himself and his mother. He is crawling, if not walking, around independently. Logical reasoning would tell us that early communication serves to reduce the spatial distance between the child and others. It may also be a means of elaborating and humanizing the child's observations of his surroundings. Luria (1961) stresses that the child receives instruction from his mother regarding his spatial explorations and retains in his memory her verbal descriptions. As these are repeated, a template is perhaps formed in the child's mind for his own future use. Current theories of learning tend to emphasize that imitative behavior in a child is not innate or instinctive, but is learned through a process of differential reinforcement. Much of the interaction of a child with his spatial environment is imitative interaction patterned after his own interaction with his mother (clinging to and putting things in his mouth) or after "model" behavior observed in his parents (example, feeding and tending babies, driving play cars, etc.). The same undoubtedly holds true of communicative patterns.

EXPERIENCE OPPORTUNITIES

Much of the experience of the young child beginning to develop language is centered around organizing conceptual relationships, and exposure to language of an older person is a constant aid to undertaking and understanding of experience. The child hears language which is much more complex than that which he uses (Brown and Fraser, 1963). Experience with reality becomes more meaningful to the child as he learns to categorize and group things together in some systematic way (Lenneberg, 1967). Labels for categories are learned by the child primarily through imitating the adult model and are, phonologically speaking, fairly rough approximations which become progressively more like the adult model as time goes on, approximating the adult pattern fairly closely by the fourth year (Jakobson and Halle, 1956; Lenneberg, 1967).

Actually, putting things in classes is a process of abstracting. As Carroll (1967) says, "a child seeing a group of cards—some white, some blue, some gray, some big, some middle-sized, some small, and so on—and calling them *cards* is therefore exhibiting the result of a fairly complex mental operation" (p. 41). To further classify cards, as a sub-category of *games* is to perform a higher order abstraction. An important function of classifying or abstracting is to aid memory. Miller (1956) indicated that memory limits of the adult is about seven plus or minus two words. How then can one account for the fact that long term storage has a much greater capacity? Miller suggests, that even though one can only remember seven items, chunks or categories within items, which in turn have many sub-categories with sub-categories, are stored and remembered. Thus, memory can be almost infinitesimal, but category organization is an essential part of memory and storage. Without such organization, memory would be greatly limited.

It is, therefore, essential for the child to have ample opportunity to interact with a richly stimulating environment which can be manipulated and classified in various ways. Much of the Montessori method of education is centered around allowing the child to interact naturally and spontaneously with the environment; it involves repeated experiences in manipulation and classification by providing materials with which the child can have repeated practice with the various senses (visual, auditory, tactile, thermic, baric, stereognostic, etc.). Stimuli in the child's environment conducive to language learning include representations of *things, actions,* and *variability* (size, shape, color, texture, weight, temperature, etc.). Carroll (1967) states that "in every language . . . we have a certain grammatical phenomenon that encapsulates concepts of *variable* and *continuum.* For we can say, 'this tree is tall. That tree is taller than this, and that tree over there is tallest of them.' *Tall* is the name of a variable—or perhaps we should say *tallness* or *height.* If we can apply the comparative or superlative degree . . . we have a variable or attribute with respect to which things can vary continuously" (p. 42).

As a child continues to interact with the environment around him, he continues to learn categorical relationships and labels for these. He also learns rules, somewhat implicitly for reasoning out or creating new conceptual relationships which seem to simplify his world and thereby create greater meaning for him (Miller, 1956). At the same time, he apparently learns (equally as implicitly) the rules for generating language constructions which express these new concepts or relationships. Relating of various classificatory experiences enables a child to make analogies across categories—a basic process in the generation of language. This is verified by common mistakes made by children in early language in such constructions as *bring, brang,* as analogous to *sing, sang; one man, two mans* an analogous to *one pan, two pans;* or *be careful!—I am becarefulling* as analogous *to behave!—I am behaving;* etc. (Moulton, 1966).

PRACTICE AND MIMICRY

"One of the most striking aspects of a child's language learning is the fact that he spends so much time at it" (Moulton, 1966, p. 2). He talks with his parents, brothers and sisters, playmates, and with himself. Much of the initial practice of language is the rehearsal of imitations in various situations. Most modern theorists deal with imitation as a product of learning (Mussen, 1966).

There is considerable evidence that semantic configurations, i.e., changes in articulation as well as development of new words, come about as a result of imitation (Sloan, 1968; Van Riper, 1963).

> Doubts about the part played by imitation must . . . be dispelled by the fact that similarities in pronunciation do exist and are very strong, for instance, between the mother and the child, and it is hard to see what mechanism other than imitation could produce this result. The effect is more noticeable, perhaps, in cases where a mother and child have a common dialect that is different from that of everyone else in the environment; in London, for example, it is not unknown for the child of a mother who has a marked Scottish accent to develop the same dialectal pronunciation even though others around him speak southern English or some other form of Cockney. (Fry, 1966, p. 191)

In order to be able to imitate others, the child has to have developed, through some sort of process, a monitoring system which enables him to produce a perceptual-motor match. This usually occurs in the practice the young baby gets during the babbling stage of speech learning.

Successive approximations toward similarity of patterns are conditioned and eventually achievement of similarity of patterns becomes a conditioned reinforcer. At this time, a child may imitate behaviors which have never been directly shaped or reinforced. (Sloan, 1968)

We are often prone to place too much emphasis upon the role of imitation because of our traditional concepts. Linguists feel that some aspects of language development cannot be accounted for entirely through imitation or operant conditioning (Miller and Irvin, 1964; Carroll, 1967), for example, syntax. Imitation, therefore, is not the entire answer to language acquisition; however, it is inconceivable that data do not contribute any linguistic information. "Any theory of any part of language acquisition requires an external model" (Smith and Miller, 1966, p. 351). No child is born speaking a natural language. He must first hear it. It is not completely clear just how hearing affects his acquisition.

CREATIVITY AND INDEPENDENCE

"A child learns much that is not taught him deliberately. Without being aware of it, an agent may create conditions that produce learning of complex responses. For example, while taking care of their children, parents often reward responses inadvertently or at least without realizing the possible far-reaching effects of their rewards. But, on the basis of this learning without tuition (teaching), many highly significant responses, motives, and attitudes become strengthened and generalize extensively" (Mussen, 1967, p. 63). One very striking difference seen in a study by Winterbottom (1958) between the environments of a group of boys with high achievement motives as compared to a group of boys with low achievement motives was that mothers of the high achievement motive group "expected earlier self-reliant and independent behavior, and gave frequent and substantial rewards for independent accomplishment" (Mussen, 1967, p. 71).

The ways in which the child becomes creative can presently only be conjectured. There are experiences which seem to affect the organism pleasurably and others which have an aversive affect (Olds and Olds, 1965). It may be that newly created concepts are the result of a desire to make experience more rewarding. In many of our experiences which are unrewarding, the reflexive behaviors described by Holland and Skinner (1965) as the "activation syndrome" are aroused to a fairly high level. Such experiences are classed as aversive in nature and might motivate the child to develop new ideas on how to avoid them, if he experiences some degree of success in this respect; increased communication may help his defense against them. On the other hand, much experience involves a reduction of the "activation syndrome" and these are referred to as appetitive in nature; they might motivate the child to develop new ideas on how to experience more similar situations, or how to perpetuate the experiences by talking about them. Thus, positive and negative reinforcement may have a bearing on the efforts which go into new organizations and conceptual creations.

Speaking seems most difficult when the organism is highly saturated with the "activation syndrome" and easiest when reflexive activation is at a minimum. This may be due to the fact that speech is highly voluntary and highly spontaneous as opposed to reflexive in nature. Many children who are extremely shy and generally fearful have also an accompanying lack of audiolinguistic skills. The relationships between prolonged anxiety, creative behavior, and language delay have only been scantily researched.

Even the most sophisticated theories of paired association or of response-reinforcement learning are incapable of accounting adequately for the intricate and complex mechanisms of syntactic production (Miller, 1958). Studies in developmental linguistics have pointed generally toward a generative theory of language acquisition. The generative theory has two sets of elements which are variously associated (Mandler, 1967). One set consists of rules, transformations, and programs, and the other set consists of words. The computer-like model in this theory implies that not all associations need to be stored; that, given rules for programming and a reservoir of stored symbol units, various out-put patterns can be programmed without the past "conditioning" of these patterns. Such a model would account for a person's being able to generate out-put patterns which are original creations, that is, have never been generated before (Chomsky, 1964).

How are rules of grammar acquired, if not strictly by associative or response conditioning? Apparently, they are learned implicitly rather than explicitly, for a child can use fairly perfect grammar and not be able to articulate or explain its underlying rules. The child's learning of syntactical rules is apparently induced by correct grammatical usuage by adults without the rules being explicitly specified. There is substantial evidence that people usually "generate" rules or hypotheses whenever the environment demands some consistancy in behavior (Mandler, 1967). Group or interpersonal interactions seem to be the triggering mechanism for development of generative competence. A further discussion of various interpersonal situations which are rather typical is presented in chapter five.

SUMMARY

Even though the child's brain has been organized, through the processes of evolution, for carrying on communicative acts, there must be a nurturing type "model" which will stimulate the child and with which he can interact before communication behavior is realized. Enrichment of communication as a tool for linking himself to his social milieu is influenced greatly by reward or reinforcement contingencies in his very early interactions with his environment, especially communicative.

REFERENCES

BROWN, R., and FRASER, C.: The acquisition of syntax. In COFER, C. N., and MUSGRAVE, B. S. (Eds.): *Verbal Behavior and Learning: Problems and Processes.* New York, McGraw-Hill, 1963.

CARROLL, J. B.: Psycholinguistics in the study of mental retardation. In SHIEFELBUSCH, R. L., COPELAND, R. H., and SMITH, J. O. (Eds.): *Language and Mental Retardation.* New York, Holt, Rinehart and Winston, Inc., 1967.

CHOMSKY, N.: Degrees of grammaticalness. In FODOR, J. A., and KATZ, J. J. (Eds.): *The Structure of Language.* Englewood Cliffs, N. J., Prentice-Hall, 1964.

ERIKSON, E. H.: *Childhood and Society.* New York, Norton, 1950. As reported by MUSSEN, P., *New Directions in Psychology III.* New York: Holt, Rinehart and Winston, Inc., 1967, p. 66.

FRY, D. B.: The development of the phonological system in the normal and the deaf child. In SMITH, F., and MILLER, G. A. (Eds.): *The Genesis of Language.* Cambridge, M.I.T. Press, 1966.

HOLLAND, J. G., and SKINNER, B. F.: *The Analysis of Behavior.* New York, McGraw-Hill, 1961.

JAKOBSON, R., and HALLE, M.: *Fundamentals of Language.* The Hague, Mouton, and Company, 1956.

LENNEBERG, E.: *The Biological Basis of Language.* New York, Wiley, 1967.

LURIA, A. R.: *The Role of Speech in the Regulation of Normal and Abnormal Behavior.* New York, Liveright, 1961.

MANDLER, G.: Verbal learning. In NEWCOMB, T. M. (Ed.): *New Directions in Psychology III.* New York, Holt, Rinehart and Winston, Inc., 1966.

MILLER, G. A.: The magical number seven, plus or minus two; some limits on our capacity for processing information. *Psychol. Rev., 63:* 81-96, 1956.

MILLER, G. A.: Free recall of redundant strings of letters. *J. Except. Psychol., 56:*484-491, 1958.

MILLER, W., and ERVIN, S.: The development of grammar in child language. In, *The Acquisition of Language.* Monograph of the Society for Research in Child Development, *29:*9-35, 1964.

MOULTON, W. G.: *A Linguistic Guide to Language Learning.* New York, The Modern Language Association, 1966.

MUSSEN, P.: Early socialization: learning and identification. In NEWCOMB, T. M. (Ed.): *New Directions in Psychology III.* New York, Holt, Rinehart and Winston, Inc., 1967.

OLDS, J., and OLDS, M.: Drives, rewards, and the brain. In NEWCOMB, T. M. (Ed.): *New Directions in Psychology II.* New York, Holt, Rinehart and Winston, Inc., 1965.

SCHIEFELBURCH, R. L., COPELAND, R. H., and SMITH, J. O.: *Language and Mental Retardation.* New York, Holt, Rinehart and Winston, Inc., 1967.

SEARS, R. R., MACCOBY, E. E., and LEVIN, H.: *Patterns of Child Rearing.* New York, Harper and Row, 1957.

SHAEFER, R. B.: Some issues for research in the study of attachment behavior. In FOSS, B. M. (Ed.): *Determinants of Infant Behavior.* New York, Wiley, 1963.

SLOAN, H. N., Jr., and MacAULAY, B. D.: *Operant Procedures in Remedial Speech and Language Training.* Boston, Houghton Mifflin Company, 1968.

SMITH, F., and MILLER, G. A.: *The Genesis of Language.* Cambridge, The M.I.T. Press, 1966.

Van RIPER, C.: *Speech Correction Principles and Methods.* Englewood Cliffs, N.J., Prentice Hall, 1963.

WINTERBOTTOM, Marian R.: The relation of need for achievement to learning experiences in independence and mastery. In ATKINSON, J. W. (Ed.): *Motives in Fantasy, Action and Society.* Princeton, N.J., Van Nostrand, 1958, pp. 453-478.

Chapter Four

MEASUREMENT OF AUDIOLINGUISTIC AND CLOSELY RELATED SKILLS

When we consider the great stress which has been placed in the past literature upon adequate "diagnosis" in the planning for therapy, it seems incongrous that there is such a dearth of standardized instrumentation in audiolinguistics. Testing procedures available are highly heterogeneous in terms of specific types of measures and extent of standardization. In selecting tests to be used for measuring audiolinguistic and related skills, one must compromise between level of standardization (and technical sophistication) and practicality in assessing the particular function to be analyzed. Inherent in this approach is the need to use instruments which are most practical but with preference to those which most closely meet *standard criteria** in the testing field. This compromise is used in the present chapter.

EVALUATION OF PERCEPTUAL FUNCTIONS RELATED TO LANGUAGE COMPETENCE**

Some skills which seem closely related to language competence and which, therefore, may be particularly important in the planning of a "related-deficit" training approach include: (1) ability to form concepts; (2) abstracting ability; (3) audiolinguistic identification; (4) audiolinguistic discrimination; (5) audiolinguistic memory, and (6) oral sterognosis. Each of these related areas and suggested ways of assessing them will be discussed briefly.

Ability to Form Concepts

Since verbal tests are at a great disadvantage in assessing intellectual function of language handicapped children, it is important to use a non-verbal conceptual test, and one which is as culture free as possible. One such test which is fairly easy to administer and which is frequently used on children ages four to ten years (the sensitive age for language acquisition) is the *Goodenough Draw-a-Man Intelligence Test* (Goodenough, 1957). It takes about ten minutes to administer and fifteen to twenty minutes to score. It can be used as a screening device and can be administered individually or to groups of children; this makes it a fairly efficient screening tool. Among other useful non-verbal tests are the *Columbia Mental Maturity Scale* (Burgemeister *et al.*, 1954), the *Leiter Internation Performance Scale* (Leiter, 1948), and the *Incomplete Man* test (Ilg and Ames, 1964).

The IPAT *Culture Fair Test of Intelligence* by Cattell (1962), purports to be free of cultural influence and this may be useful along with the *Goodenough Draw-a-Man Intelligence Test* in assessing children of widely varying cultural backgrounds. The "Culture Fair" test can be administered to an individual or groups of children.

Ability to Abstract

Since categorizing and abstracting are functionally related to language acquisition, it is essential to evaluate the child who has language delay in these important areas. The *Peabody Picture Vocabulary Test* (Dunn, 1959) measures receptive semantic abstracting ability of the child and takes only about

---

*American Psychological Association. *Standards for Educational and Psychological Test Manuals*. Washington, D. C., American Psychological Association, Inc., 1966.

**Organismic variables directly affect *performance* primarily only in cases of neuromotor pathology. For suggestions regarding neuromotor evaluation of the brain-injured child, the reader is referred to current literature bearing on expressive language problems of organic origin (see Mecham *et al.*, 1966; and Mysak, 1968). For tests of general neuromotor ability, consult Roach and Kephart (1966), Ayres (1967).

fifteen minutes to administer. It was designed to be administered as an individual test but can be adapted for groups. This test, however, may be heavily influenced by cultural background.

Some tests of intelligence have subtests which measure the specific ability of the child to classify. An example of this is the *Culture Fair Test of Intelligence.* Norms for such subtests are usually not separately available, so it may be necessary to get some rough local norms by administering the subtest to a hundred or so normal children. (One of the shortcomings of a subtest within a larger test is that its reliability is usually questionable when used only by itself.)

A test designed and standardized to measure abstracting ability in brain-injured children was developed by Irwin and Hammil (1964).

Auditory Identification

Accuracy of correct identification of linguistic symbols is an important aspect to be assessed in the child suspected of having a language disability. A test designed to assess accuracy of auditory identification in children has recently been standardized (Mecham, 1969). This test, entitled *Test of Listening Accuracy in Children* (Mecham and Jex, 1968), was standardized on 2,000 elementary school children. It can be administered on either a group or individual basis and normative scores are available for kindergarten through sixth grade levels.

Auditory Discrimination

Several tests of auditory discrimination have been developed for use with speech handicapped individuals. Some which are widely used include: *Auditory Discrimination Test* (Wepman, 1958); the *Templin Tests of Sound and Word Discrimination* (Templin, 1957); the Boston University *Picture-type Speech Sound Discrimination Test* (Pronovost and Dumbleton, 1953) and a *Test of Sound Discrimination for Use with Cerebral Palsy Children* (Irwin and Jensen, 1963).

The *Wepman* Test, standardized for children from five through eight years of age, consists of two equated forms (forms 1 and 2), forty items each. It is individually administered and explicit instructions are available in the test manual for giving the tests. The *Templin Test of Sound Discrimination* is comprised of fifty items standardized on children aged six through eight. Her second test, a word discrimination test using pictures, was standardized on children aged three through five. Only one form of each of these tests was developed, and they are not available as autonomously published tests. The *Boston University* test consists of thirty-six items and was standardized on 434 first grade children. It takes approximately fifteen to twenty minutes to administer. The *Irwin* and *Jensen* test was designed specifically for use with cerebral palsy children; no norms are as yet available for its use with other groups of children.

Auditory Memory

An important topic for evaluation is the child's short-term auditory memory, since this is functionally related to language development. Tests of memory are available as subtests of standardized tests, e.g., the *Stanford-Binet* and the *WISC* tests. A fairly complete test of short-term memory was recently compiled by Kohler (1968) consisting of memory for digits, memory for nonsense words, and memory for sentences. It was tentatively standardized on children from first through sixth grade.

Oral Stereognosis

Procedures for evaluating oral stereognostic skills in children have recently been explored, and some autonomously developed tests may soon be available. McDonald (1967) and others (Bosma, 1967) have described some standard test procedures which can be used in assessing this skill.

THE AUDIOLINGUISTIC LADDER

Studies of the neuro-ontogenesis of speech and language (Pennfield and Roberts, 1959; Lenneberg, 1966a, 1966b, 1967) strongly suggest a time-locked relationship between chronological age and emergence of various milestones of language development. This relationship seems to be centered around cerebral maturation and plasticity for certain types of neuro-behavioral organization. There seem to be definite periods in a child's life before which he cannot utilize his environment to facilitate a particular behavior pattern and after which it becomes progressively more difficult to facilitate its emergence. Mysak (1968, p. 79) has stressed the importance of considering age limitations on language acquisition when considering the actual emergences in a particular child being evaluated.

It is evident that the various types of language behavior do not all emerge at the same time. For example, children usually begin to use correct word combinations at about two to two and one-half years, but do not begin to count two or more numbers in correct order (except in repetition) until three to three and one-half. By seven years most children can count to fifty or more. They do not usually name any particular color accurately until three and one-half, but have mastered most colors by four and one-half. Thus, we see that not only do various verbal behaviors begin to emerge at differing ages, but they also emerge at different rates. Developmental evaluations should tell us not only the *age of onset* of the verbal behaviors of a particular child, but also how he compares to expectations in terms of *rate of emergence* of various skills.

A developmental test, then should show some measure of the various skills over several points in time. Most developmental tests available only roughly achieve this task, mainly because it is easier to assess the presence or absence of a given skill than it is to assess its rate of maturation.

Several developmental tests are currently available and are at least a beginning step in the objectification of the developmental evaluation.

A test which has proved especially useful with pre-school children, in that it utilizes the parent as the informant and does not require that the child be tested directly, is the *Verbal Language Development Scale* (Mecham, 1959). This test was an extension of the communication part of the *Vineland Social*

Maturity Scale and consists of developmental language items contained in various standardized mental tests.

The *Houston Test for Language Development* (Crabtree, 1963) is a test which identifies primarily the *onset* of certain language milestones. The preliminary edition was standardized for children aged six months through three years (based upon a norm group of 113 children). In 1963, the test was expanded with additional norms to include test items for children up through age six. It is administered individually and takes about one hour.

The *Peabody Picture Vocabulary Test* (Dunn, 1959) measures the progression of a single language skill (i.e., receptive vocabulary) from two years to adult level. Two forms of the test have been standardized on approximately 4,012 subjects. The test scores can be translated into mental age, IQ, or percentile from tables available in the manual. In the case of language testing, the terminology can be changed to "language age," "LQ," or language "percentile" since it samples normal language function. The test is conventionally administered individually rather than to a group. It takes from fifteen to thirty minutes to administer.

Another evaluative procedure which measures the progression of a single language function, i.e., *length of verbal expressions,* is one which has been used by linguists and speech pathologists for over forty years (Nice, 1925; McCarthy, 1930; Smith, 1935; Davis, 1937; Templin, 1957; Winitz, 1959; Darley and Moll, 1960; Shriner, 1967). The internal consistency of this measure appears to be excellent, but temporal reliability is not as impressive (Fisher, 1934; Griffith and Ingalls, 1968). Although it is a somewhat cumbersome device, it is generally considered a good clinical method of assessing language maturity in the child.

A recently constructed measuring instrument which assesses both the *onset* and *progressive maturation* of a number of language skills is the *Utah Test of Language Development* (Mecham *et al.,* 1967). Evidence for the construct validity of the test lies in the method of construction, that is, language items from numerous standardized tests were included together and were arranged in accordance with age norms on the original sources. The test was then standardized as an integrated test on a representative population of 535* children ages 2 through 16. The test is administered individually and takes from one-half to three-fourths of an hour.

Excellent diagnostic procedures for assessing *disorders* of language in preschool children have been reported by Bangs (1968). From the *Language and Learning Assessment* test battery, a profile can be obtained which trouble shoots relative difficulties in various areas of language reception and expression. Although no norms are reported specifically for this test, its items were derived from various well standardized sources.

In addition to assessing language in terms of age of onset and rate of progression in various skills, the qualitative analysis of language function, i.e., analysis of *language structure,* gives additional insight as to the elaborateness or restrictedness of structure (Bernstein, 1964). A discussion of this kind of assessment will be the topic of the next section of this chapter.

ANALYSIS OF QUALITY OF
LINGUISTIC STRUCTURE

Analysis of quality of linguistic structure (i.e., morphology and syntax) is a more molecular approach to language evaluation in contrast to the molar approaches described in the previous sections. If the child falls down on the *developmental ladder,* it is logical to take a look at his *language structure* and see where he is having trouble primarily. The structural analysis gives insight into the kind of things which can be incorporated into language training or which eventually go to make up what we observe on the molar level.

There are, generally speaking, two perspectives in the analysis of language structure (Chomsky, 1967), *linquistic competence* (an implicit knowledge of the rules governing linguistic production) and *linguistic performance* (the actual language output of the individual).

---

*This is a larger sample than that reported in the manual; it includes data collected since publication of the 1967 edition in the test. Normative ages for the items and total scores remained relatively unchanged as a result of the enlarged normative sample.

The language measures which have been described in the previous section have little to do with the assessment of the child's handling of morphology and syntax. The instruments available for this latter type of assessment are scarce, exploratory, and not well standardized; but they are much better than no instruments at all. Two tests of syntax and morphology warrant special attention because they seen to cover fairly well the two perspectives mentioned above, namely, *competence* and *performance.*

Linguistic Competence

A test recently developed and reported by Carrow (1968) assesses the child's ability to *comprehend* the structure of language. Test items were originally tried on 159 normal children; nine age groups each represented a six-month age span between 2-10 and 7-9 years. Eighty-six boys and seventy-three girls were represented in this group. The items developed permitted "assessment of oral language comprehension without requiring language expression from the child" (Carrow, 1968, p. 103). To avoid testing lexical rather than grammatical knowledge, vocabulary was used which is learned early in the developmental sequence. The test was again "administered in a preliminary form to 40 children between the ages of 2-6 and 6-6 in order to standardize the procedure, to revise specific items, and to determine the order of presentation of the items" (Carrow, 1968, p. 104). It is the feeling of the author of the test that additional work needs to be done on it and more children need to be studied. In the meantime, the test may give the teacher or clinician considerable insight into the child's comprehension skills. The major segments of the test are outlined below.

Form Classes and Function Words
Morphological Constructions
Grammatical Categories
Syntactic Structure

Linguistic Performance

A test which promises to be a useful one, when more rigorously standardized, was developed by Berko (1958). The test was designed primarily to assess the child's acquisition of morophological rules. The 28 items on this test take approximately fifteen minutes to give. It is administered individually, and assesses the child's linguistic performance in the following:

> Plural
> Past Tense
> Derived Adjective
> Diminuitive and Compound
> Third Person Singular
> Singular and Plural Possessive
> Comparative and Superlative of Adjective
> Progressive and Derived Agentive or Compound
> Compound Words

Other procedures which may be of interest to the reader include those proposed by Weir (1962), Braine (1963), Brown and Fraser (1954), Miller and Ervin (1964), Brown and Bellugi (1964), Menyuk (1964), Lee (1966), and Kirk and McCarthy (1968).

SUMMARY

Diagnostic or evaluative study of the child should provide the ground work for planning remediation of related deficits as well as language. It should reflect *milestones* which have emerged and extent of their emergence in comparison with age of the child. It should also give qualitative insight into *restrictedness* or *elaborateness* of language structure in terms of both language competence and language performance. This chapter discusses some evaluative procedures which should be of help in accomplishing this task.

REFERENCES

AYRES, A. J.: *Southern California Test Battery for Assessment of Dysfunction.* Los Angeles, Western Psychological Services, 1967.
BERKO, J.: The child's learning of English morphology. *Word, 14*:150-177, 1958.

BERNSTEIN, B.: Aspects of language and learning in the genesis of the social process. In HYMES, D. (Ed.), *Language in Culture and Society*. New York, Harper and Row, 1964.

BANGS, T. E.: *Language and Learning Disorders of the Pre-Academic Child*. New York, Appleton-Century-Crofts, 1968.

BRAINE, M. D. S.: Ontogeny of English phrase structure: the first phrase. *Language, 39*:1-13, 1963.

BROWN, R., and FRASER, C.: The acquisition of syntax. In BELLUGI, U., and BROWN, R.: *The Acquisition of Language*. Monograph of the Society for Research in Child Development, *29*:43-79, 1964.

BROWN, R., and BELLUGI, U.: Three processes in the child's acquisition of syntax. *Harvard Educ. Rev., 34*:133-152, 1964.

BURGEMEISTER, B., and BLUM, L. H.: *Columbia Mental Maturity Scale*. New York, Harcourt, Brace and World, Inc., 1954.

CARROW, M. A., Sr.: The development of auditory comprehension of language structure in children. *JSHD, 33*:99-111, 1968.

CATTELL, R. B.: *Culture Fair Intelligence Test-Scale I*. Champaign, Ill., Institute for Personality and Ability Testing, 1962.

CHOMSKY, N.: The formal nature of language. In LENNEBERG, E. H.: *The Biological Basis of Language*. New York, Wiley, 1967.

CRABTREE, M.: *Houston Test for Language Development*. Houston, The Houston Test Company, 1963.

DARLEY, F. L., and MOLL, K. L.: Reliability of language measures and size of language sample. *JSHR*, 166-173, 1960.

DAVIS, E. A.: The development of linguistic skills in twins and singletons from age five to ten years. *Institute of Child Welfare Monograph Series, No. 14*. Minneapolis, University of Minnesota Press, 1937.

DUNN, L. J.: *The Peabody Picture Vocabulary Test*. Minneapolis, American Guidance Service 1959.

FISHER, M. S.: Language patterns of preschool children. *Child Development, 8*:69-79, 1934.

GOODENOUGH, F. L.: *Goodenough Draw-a-Man Intelligence Test*. New York, Psychological Corporation, 1957.

GRIFFITH, D. L., and INGALLS, S. I.: A Criterion Related Validity Study of the Utah Test of Language Development. Salt Lake City, University of Utah, unpublished Master's thesis, 1968.

ILG, F., and AMES, L.: *School Readiness*. New York, Harper and Row, 1964.

IRWIN, O. C., and JENSEN, P. J.: A test of sound discrimination for use with cerebral palsied children. *Cerebral Palsy Review, 24*:5-11, 1963.

IRWIN, O. C., and HAMMIL, D. D.: An abstraction test for use with cerebral palsied children. *Cerebral Palsy Review, 24*:3-9, 1964.

KIRK, S. A., McCARTHY, J. J., and KIRK, W. D.: *Illinois Test of Psycholinguistic Abilities (Revised)*. Urbana, Illinois, University of Illinois Press, 1968.

KOHLER, R.: The Validation of a Screening Test of Auditory Perceptual Abilities of Elementary School Children. Salt Lake City, University of Utah, unpublished doctoral dissertation, 1967.

LEE, L.: Developmental sentence types: a method for comparing normal and deviant syntactical development. *JSHD, 31*:311-330, 1966.

LEITER, R. G.: *Leiter International Performance Scale.* Washington, D. C., Psychological Service Center Press, 1948.

LENNEBERG, E. H.: Speech development: its anatomical and physiological concomitants. In CARTERETTE (Ed.): *Brain Function: Speech, Language, and Communication.* Berkeley, University of California Press 1966a.

LENNEBERG, E. H.: The natural history of language. In SMITH, F., and MILLER, G. A. (Eds.): *The Genesis of Language.* Cambridge, The M.I.T. Press, 1966b.

LENNEBERG, E. H.: *The Biological Basis of Language.* New York, Wiley, 1967.

McCARTHY, D.: The language development of the preschool child. *Institute of Child Welfare Monograph Series, No. 4.* Minneapolis, University of Minnesota Press, 1930.

McDONALD, E. T., and AUNGST, L. F.: Studies in oral sensorimotor function. In BOSMA, J. F.: *Symposium on Oral Sensation and Perception.* Springfield, Ill., Charles C. Thomas, 1967.

MECHAM, M. J.: *Verbal Language Development Scale.* Minneapolis, American Guidance Service, 1959.

MECHAM, M. J.: Standardization Report on "Test of Listening Accuracy in Children." Salt Lake City, University of Utah, Speech and Hearing Clinic, 1968.

MECHAM, M. J., BERKO, M. J., and BERKO, F. G.: *Communication Training in Childhood Brain Damage.* Springfield, Ill., Charles C. Thomas, 1966.

MECHAM, M. J., JEX, J. L., and JONES, J. D.: *Utah Test of Language Development.* Salt Lake City, Utah, Communication Research Associates, 1967.

MECHAM, M. J., JEX, J. L., and Jones, J. D.: *Test of Listening Accuracy in Children.* Provo, Utah, Brigham Young University Press, 1969.

MENYUK, P.: Comparison of grammar of children with functionally deviant and normal speech. *JSHR, 7*:109-121, 1964.

MILLER, W., and ERVIN, S.: The development of grammar in child language. In BELLUGI, E., and BROWN, R.: *The Acquisition of Language.* Monograph of the Society for Research in Child Development, *29*:9-35, 1964

MYSAK, E. D.: *Neuroevolutional Approach to Cerebral Palsy and Speech.* New York, Columbia University Teachers College Press, 1968.

NICE, M. M.: Length of sentences as a criterion of a child's progress in speech. *J. Educ. Psychol., 16*:370-379, 1925.

PENFIELD, W., and ROBERTS, L.: *Speech and Brain Mechanisms.* Princeton, Princeton University Press, 1959.

PRONOVOST, W., and DUMBLETON, C.: A picture-type speech sound discrimination test. *JSHD, 18*:258-266, 1953.

ROACH, E. G., and KEPHART, N. C.: *The Purdue Perceptual-Motor Survey.* Columbus, Charles E. Merrill, 1966.

SHRINER, T. H.: A comparison of selected measures with psychological scale values of language development. *JSHR, 10*:828-835, 1967.

SMITH, M. E.: A study of some of the factors influencing the development of the sentence in preschool children. *J. Gen. Psychol., 46*:182-212, 1935.

TEMPLIN, M. C.: *Certain Language Skills in Children: Child Welfare Monographs Series, No. 26.* Minneapolis, University of Minnesota Press, 1957.

WEIR, R. H.: *Language in the Crib.* The Hague, Mouton and Company, 1962.

WEPMAN, J. M.: *Auditory Discrimination Test.* Chicago, 950 East 59th Street, 1958.

WINITZ, H.: Language skills of male and female kindergarten children. *JSHR, 2*:377-386, 1959.

Chapter Five

FACILITATION OF AUDIOLINGUISTIC SKILLS IN LANGUAGE DELAYED CHILDREN

INTRODUCTION

Ayres (1967) aptly stated that the "child develops according to a given sequence, each step dependent—to a certain extent—upon previous steps . . . Sensory [and motor] integrative processes occurring in the early years of life are critical to the later development of the cognitive functions of academic learning" (p. 203).

The nature and extent of oral communication milestone emergences are usually fairly similar from one child to another of a particular mental age, irrespective of race, geographical region or culture. Children normally begin to talk at approximately 12 to 14 months (mental age). Various levels of social competence are achieved in oral communication as the mental age of the child increases. Before the child's second birthday he uses short sentences and has a vocabulary of 25 words or more. Toward the end of his second year the child is using up to three words per sentence, but sentences at this age are for the most part grammatically incomplete. Before his third birthday, he gives a simple account of his experiences and tells stories that can be understood. During the third year the child begins using pronouns and plurals and verbalizes his toilet needs. By the end of the fourth or beginning of the fifth year, he begins learning nursery rhymes, names of colors, names of coins, and he relates fanciful tales. By the time he is eight years of age, he is able to retell familar stories and can define meanings of several words. By his tenth year, the average child retells jokes and short stories, uses the telephone independently, and produces all of his speech sounds correctly. By sixteen years, he is able to use intelligent and persuasive speech in a discussion of current events, politics, etc.

Experiences which are introduced or skills that are expected to be mastered which are beyond the readiness or capacity of the child at a given stage in his development can greatly impede the process of maturation.

According to a recent theory of language development reported by Lenneberg (1967), the child engages in language "behavior as if by resonance; he is maturationally ready but will not begin to perform unless properly stimulated. If exposed to the stimuli, he becomes socially 'excited' as a resonator may become excited when exposed to a given range of sound frequencies ... An impoverished social input may entail permanently impoverished behavioral patterns" (pp. 373-374). Likewise, unnatural social input (such as we find in much of our analytic drill work) may actually impede the unfolding process in language development. The things considered by Lenneberg to be innate in language behavior are "modes of categorization" and "the general mode of the actualization process but no particular aspect of the realized structure" (p. 394). Thus, *particular features* of syntax, phonology, or semantics which vary from one language to another are not considered innate. However, "the *processes* by which the ... structure of a natural language comes about are deeply-rooted, species-specific innate propensities of man's biological nature" (p. 394).

The developmental frame of reference is used in the present chapter on facilitation of verbal language development because it is important that the teacher or clinician be familiar with sensitive periods for the various developmental milestones; they should know not only what ages are too early for their stimulation, but also what ages are too late for effective acquisition. This approach also implies the biological readiness of related processes and *their* interaction with the environment; thus, two major forces are acting together in the developmental process, namely: (1) strengthening organismic variables *within* the child which are responsible for his biological maturation for language, and (2) creating a facilitative environment which will be an optimal place for his developmental interactions in learning. These two forces will be the topic of discussion for the remaining part of this chapter.

STRENGTHENING ORGANISMIC VARIABLES

Some of the deficits in the basic sensory-motor systems commonly found in children with learning (language) disability include: (1) dyspraxia, i.e., coordination difficulties resulting from disintegrated somatosensory input, especially of discriminative, kinesthetic, and tactile perception (Ayres, 1967); (2) bilateral and postural disorientation, which may include poor inhibition of primitive postural reactions, poor coordination of the simultaneous use of both sides of the body, and poor left and right discrimination (Ayres, 1967); (3) space and form perceptual confusion—visual, tactile, and kinesthetic (Frostig, 1967; Rood, 1954); and (4) auditory perceptual confusion including poor memory, inaccurate discrimination, and difficulty in deciphering or organizing temporally sequenced patterns.

The general approaches to treatment for these problems are rather implicit, biologically oriented approaches and are usually aimed at establishment of more normal basic perceptual-motor integration in the various hierarchies of neural-behavioral patterns. The premise is used that given more adequate perceptual-motor skills, the child can better interact with conventional learning contingencies. Procedures often differ drastically between the various perceptual-motor training methods. Bobaths (1964) use reflex inhibiting and automatic movements to encourage higher righting and equilibrium reactions. Delacato (1966) encourages primitive movement from various levels of neurological organization, and trains for dominance of one cerebral hemisphere over the other. Kephart (1960), Frostig (1964) and Winterhaven Lions (1965) use sensory-motor sequencing patterns to encourage neocortical (voluntary) generalization of posture and balance;

object manipulation; object receipt and/or propulsion; temporal synchrony, rhythm and sequence; spatial organization of form, size, and patterns; sensory-motor match (or copying); and body image and differentiation. These programs can be put to good use, depending on the general needs of the child.*

The two most important organismic variables involved in audiolinguistic competence seem to be auditory perception and oral stereognosis (Shelton *et al.*, 1967, p. 222). The approaches to remedying these related organismic deficits are of necessity more structured than those used in actual language training. Some examples of how these specific functions might be approached in training are enumerated below. *Since performance is directly dependent upon competence, the latter is considered as a primary concern in the present manual.* No amount of work on performance can be fruitful without first establishing competence. For an excellent reference on establishing better performance in the brain-injured child, see Mysak 1968.

Auditory Perception

Auditory training includes facilitation of auditory recognition, auditory discrimination, auditory stimulus recall and scanning, auditory categorization and abstraction. The following suggested activities are not meant to be model, but merely illustrative of the kinds of activities which can be used to facilitate auditory skills. We assume in these activities that hearing acuity is normal or corrected. Materials needed include approximately six differing sound objects such as: bell, wood cylinder, toy cricket, bicycle horn, whistle, toy xylophone, wood clicker, etc.

Recognition. *Stage one,* present one object auditorily while the child's back is turned or he is blindfolded. Then have the child look at all objects and point to the one he heard. Repeat until he identifies all objects auditorily. *Stage two,* present two objects at once with no visual clues being given and have the child identify which two of the entire group were presented. Repeat this activity until he identifies all possible pairs of objects. *Stage three,* present

---

*The reader would do well to study these original references in detail in order to gain more insight into their possible use in readiness training.

three objects simultaneously and have the child identify which three of the entire group he heard. Repeat activity until he identifies all possible combinations of three. When recognition of gross sounds is mastered, use speech materials involving pictures as follows. *Stage one,* present two pictures and name one of them. Have the child point to the one named. *Stage two,* present three pictures and name one of them. Have the child point to the one named. *Stage three,* present two pictures and name one, pronouncing phonemes one-half second apart. Begin with two syllable words; then use three, four, five, and six syllables respectively.

Discrimination. *Stage one,* present two pictures simultaneously and name one of the pictures correctly and the other picture incorrectly. For example, if you have a picture of *feet* and one of *money,* you could say "seat-money." The child's task would be to point to money. *Stage two,* use three pictures, one receiving correct and two receiving foil labels. The child's task is to point to the picture correctly named. *Stage three,* present a picture to the child. Name the picture either correctly or incorrectly. The child is to tell you whether you named the picture correctly. Practice until he has mastered accurate discriminations for a nucleus vocabulary.

Stimulus Recall and Scanning. *Stage one,* present two of the auditory objects without visual clue and have the child tell which objects and point to the one which was heard first. *Stage two,* present three auditory objects about one second apart and have the child select them and arrange in correct order of presentation. *Stage three,* increase the object presentation to four, one second apart, then five and then six (increase number only when child can successfully complete each level 80% of the time). *Stage four,* have six playing-card-sized pictures. Name three before showing all six to the child. Have the child pick out the ones named and place them in correct sequence (as named). Increase the total number of pictures to seven and name four; to eight and name five; etc. Give the child two different simple instructions and then encourage him to carry them out in the order which you gave them. Increase the instructions to three, then four, etc.

Auditory Categorization and Abstraction. A procedure described by Irwin and Hammil (1964) for assessing auditory abstracting and categorizing ability in children can be used also as an example of kinds of activities which can stimulate development of these skills. Questions can be clustered around experience units as in the following example. With "mealtime" serving as the nucleus experience, children can be asked:

Which is hot: soup, ice cream, butter, coke?
Which is cold: soup, ice cream, meat, corn?
Which is a vegetable: meat, ice cream, peas, cereal?
Which do we cut with: fork, dish, spoon, knife?
What time is lunch: morning evening, noon, night?

Oral Stereognosis

In oral sensory-perceptive training, the child must first be oriented to various form materials visually through matching practice. The various forms which may be used have been suggested by McDonald and Soloman (1967) and by Shelton *et al.* (1967). The forms should be approximately one-half inch by one-half inch in overall dimensions. In order to orient the child as to what is to be done, the child may be asked to do manual stereognostic exercises by pulling various forms out of a paper bag (blindfolded) and revealing by feel what they are.

Recognition. The unknown forms are placed in the child's mouth one at a time without any visual cues as to their identity. The child's task is to match up the form which is in the mouth with an identical form placed among others on a board in front of him. (Another technique is to have elevated figures or forms on blocks which the child traces over with his tongue. His task in this case is to recognize which block figure he traced.)

Discrimination. The same basic forms may be used. The task is to place first one form in the child's mouth for a few moments until he indicates he has had a chance to identify it, remove it and then immediately place either the same form or another different form in the child's mouth. He is to merely tell you whether the forms which were placed in his mouth were the same or different. Make the tasks more challenging by using forms which are similar in shape and different in size, or merely slightly different in length, etc.

Stimulus Recall and Scanning. The task is to recall the order in which two or more forms have been placed in the mouth (one at a time). Begin with the "base" level and work up to several forms in each task. Place forms in the mouth consecutively at the rate of about three seconds each. Have the child also identify the order in which the forms were placed in the mouth.

Categorization and Abstraction. Basic form types or "classes" are given the child as shown in Figure 3. Variations of these basic types are placed in the child's mouth and he is to categorize each form by identifying the form class to which it belongs.

Selecting Children for Training. Although norms are not yet available for stereognostic skills of children at various age levels, it is practical to check some 25 or 30 "normal" children of a given age and plot a distribution of their scores. Select then any children of that age level who fall more than one standard deviation below the average for that group as candidates for special training.

STRENGTHENING AN ELICITING ENVIRONMENT

Strengthening the environment to facilitate language "resonance" includes *structuring* an eliciting environment with which the child can properly interact linguistically. This includes strengthening the stimulus variables which will provide for

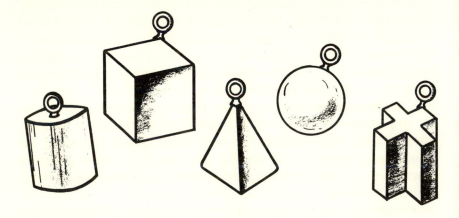

Figure 3.   Basic categories of forms for oral stereognostic training. (From McDonald, 1967)

optimal motivation and developmental "triggering" in the training process. *Ethologists have demonstrated well that actualization of any species-specific behavior depends upon "triggering" of such behavior by certain combinations of environmental stimuli at specified maturational periods.*

It is assumed that to utilize redundancies of the language to advantage (that is, perceive language with the greatest amount of proficiency), the listener "possesses, implicitly, an enormous knowledge of the statistics of the language" (Shannon and Weaver, 1949). If one can not, for some reason, take advantage of redundancy, reception of information can break down at the slightest introduction of noise (Staniland, 1966). It is probable that learning of statistics of a language is enriched by a great deal of *social interaction* or natural learning as well as through the more explicit learning (Moulton, 1966). This is evidenced by the fact that three or four year old children can speak their native language with much greater facility than a foreigner who has formally studied the language for five or six years or more (of course, age of learning may also be a prime variable). Meanings of words are normally learned, not by having symbolic objects or pictures presented with the word, but rather by "observing (mostly quite unconsciously) the [reality and] context in which the words occur" (Moulton, 1966, p. 101).

Since language "triggering" must be geared to developmental or maturational stages in order to be effective, it is essential to keep in mind the maturational stage of the child in language development and to so structure the environment as to facilitate the next stage in the maturation ladder. (For a list of various milestones of language development and sensitive ages for their emergence see Table 1, pages 6-7.) In addition to knowing the developmental level of the child in language, it is also important to know whether the child is physiologically ready in skills closely related to the desired language level. Developmental tests of perceptual and motor skills should have been administered (see chapter four).

Keeping in mind the essential social nature of audiolinguistic functions, we might set up the following objectives for strengthening a more facilitative environment: (a) providing for real or contrived experiences which are conducive to normal development of verbal language, and (b) providing an interaction between experience-concepts and labeling-competence.

Providing Real or Contrived Experiences.

General principles for psychological and experiential enrichment for the child have been summarized by Beasley (1956). The emotional climate in which learning will best be facilitated is one in which the child feels accepted, respected, secure, and thus, that he belongs. He also experiences satisfactions and pleasures. Only within such an enriched emotional climate can we expect to get full dimensional growth around a nucleus of developmental stimulations.

Principles underlying the actual acquisition of language are closely related to those involved in acquisition of concepts and values derived directly from various concrete experiences.

> Our experiences with the world registers within us in the form of concepts, values and feelings for things, language, skills and habits. They then become the controlling elements in determining what we try to do and how well we do it.
>
> When through experience we get a mental picture of objects or forces which make up the world, we have a concept, which immediately becomes our set for any further perception of that same thing.
>
> While concepts are forming through experience, the individual is also learning what value each of the objects and forces has for him through his impressions of how each of them affects him. This sense of value becomes part of each concept and determines how he feels about it. This tends to influence his behavior toward that thing.
>
> As the concept forms in our minds we learn symbols for the whole concept and for each of its parts or qualities and these symbols become part of the concept also. (Woodruff, 1961, p. 63)

Thus, if labels are not supplied in experience settings but are taught separately and apart from experience, such as in the case of word drill lists, they are not learned as an integral part of the child's concepts and therefore have little functional meaning or practical use as communication units. If the teacher or clinician supplies the verbal symbols "that's rain, that's snow, that's sun, etc." at the time that the child is experiencing a specific concept, then that label may be used as a reference for any further learning of more general concepts, for example, "weather."

Motivation and communication interaction in structured life situations between children in a group are of primary importance in audiolinguistic training. As the child acquires experiences on a very concrete level, specific and appropriate labels must be supplied at the time that the child is experiencing and forming the concepts related thereto, thus *facilitating* the labelings' becoming an integral part of the concept. As labels are given in real life experiences, every possible sensory and motor avenue (touch, handle, see, hear, taste, and smell) must be used to clarify the concepts and enrich the association with a verbal label.

Segmental drill has a place in the development of many types of motor skills (including articulation). Even drill, however, should be preceded by an accurate concept of the way in which the motor configuration must be performed. Such concepts are usually difficult to achieve in extremely young children. In *language facilitation* we should avoid segmented drill and orient practice into functional life situations with repeated opportunity to engage in whole speech responses such as words and phrases with a good model ever present. Encouragement toward listening maturation will enable the child to gradually recognize differences which exist between his own verbalizations and those of the model and gradually change his patterns for more accurate production. This is aided by a skilled teacher or clinician who will watch the child's performance and make suggestions for changes toward improvement of skills.

It would be good, in the language training situation, to create an atmosphere of specific geographic locations or events which would be similar to particular experience units for the children in daily life. Some suggestive "structured" experiences which might approximate the normal environment where nucleus corpuses of language are exchanged are listed below.

1. Direct Purposeful experiences (any real life events which are labeled by way of instructions, questions, explanations, persuasive urging, exclamations, or general conversation).

2. Contrived experiences (such as play store, service

station, model airplane, clay modeling or other creative art, sand building, water play, etc.).

3. Dramatized experiences (such as stories, skits, or make-believe play involving dress-up, play family, police-gangster, Indian-cowboy, play school, cooking, beauty parlor, baby tending, etc.).

4. Demonstrations (such as showing how things work, what something is made of, or how to do something).

5. Field trips (including things to see, feel, hear, smell, actions, how things differ, ect.).

Actual field trips are next best to purposive experiences, and if these are not feasible, artificial experiences contrived or dramatized within the classroom can be effective alternatives. One advantage of structured experiences in the classroom is that labels can be supplied at the moment of experience and therefore can more easily become part of the experience concept. *Nucleus* categorical experiences are important since they are most often encountered in daily life activities and are more likely to be experienced by the child when he is on his own outside of the classroom or therapy situation. For a rich resource of illustrative real-life or experience oriented activities, consult Bangs (1968) and Low (1969).

Encouraging Interaction Between Concept- and Language-Organization

Labeling and Vocabulary Development. Vygotsky (1952) has said that, "The sensory material and the word are both inseparable parts of concept formation" (p. 52). We have noted earlier that the label is paired with an experience and becomes part of the concept of the experience. Lenneberg (1967) states that we should consider concept formation the primary cognitive process and naming the secondary cognitive process. "Words are not labels of concepts completed earlier and stored away; they are the labels of a *categorization process or family of such processes" (p. 333).*

Meaningful experiences should then allow the child to interact and develop concepts which are commonly described in language of children and at the same time to hear the words which

TABLE 2

ACTION WORDS WHICH COMMONLY APPEAR IN THE EARLIER
STAGES OF LANGUAGE (LANGUAGE AGE 2 1/2). ONLY THE
NOUN–VERB PARTS OF THE SENTENCES ARE SHOWN HERE*

like a piggy bank	see cactus
I go	he want
like a garbage man	Anthony write
she go	find it
like a vacuum	Anthony can
take the monkey	drink it
get coffee	I take
take it	I'm going
stop the ball	fix it
stop it	bring it
I'm fixing	take a book
you take	light is
take the hat	I hope
cross the street	excuse me
fix the music	make it
fix the donkey	Bobo has
get powder	Daddy give
Mommy take	I spilled
lock the door	Daddy have
Mommy go	Daddy had
doggie bite	Daddy dance
take Daddy's	Daddy put
take the glasses	see the doggie
kitty likes	

*Taken from Weir (1962).

appropriately label the concepts. Thus in a typical preschool class or therapy group, the children will interact with and receive their model from other children and from the teacher or clinician. For those children who do not interact readily, use of systematic reinforcement to motivate more frequent interaction should be very helpful.

Early experiences center around categories of *things, actions,* and the *manner* in which things and actions *vary.* Experiences should provide opportunities for interactions which are rich in the categorizing process and which can be labeled with nouns, verbs, and variability words (i.e., open classes of adjectives and adverbs). Tables 2, 3 and 4 give common categories and subcategories of

TABLE 3

NOUN CATEGORIES AND SUB–CATEGORIES WHICH ARE FAIRLY
REPRESENTATIVE OF NUCLEUS EXPERIENCES IN YOUNG CHILDREN

Categories	Sub-Categories
Body	arm leg foot face back front nose hair, etc.
Car	wheel door seat engine tire gas water oil, etc.
City	house building street lights fire-engines policeman cars people, etc.
Family	mother father grandparents uncle aunt brother sister baby, etc.
Farm	tools machinery buildings fields plants horse cow sheep pig chickens, etc.
Food	vegetable meat egg fruit nut dairy hay, etc.
Home	furniture family dog cat automobile garage shrubs mailbox rooms, etc.
Money	penny nickle dime quarter 25 cents 50 cents half dollar dollar, etc.
Year	month week day hour holiday birthday aniversary, etc.
People	nationalities boy girl man woman lady children, etc.
School	teacher pupil desk playground study recess test pencil book paper, etc.
Seasons	spring summer fall autumn winter, etc.

TABLE 4

CATEGORIES OF VARIABILITY AND NUCLEUS WORDS
WHICH FALL INTO THE VARIOUS CATEGORIES

Category	Specific Nucleus Words
Time	already early late new past recent sometime soon then today when while ever never ago always since, etc.
Color	black brown gray green pink red white yellow blue orange silver, etc.
Manner	active funny lazily serious successful tired mean weak strong, etc.
Distance	further near here far long close, etc.
Number	both one two three four five six seven eight nine ten eleven twelve twenty hundred thousand million
Shape	square straight crooked round rectangle triangle oval, etc.
Amount	approximately equal many all full half most much some, etc.
Size	large small little short big, etc.
Direction	down toward up front forward left west away back side right east south north, etc.
Temperature	cool cold hot warm freezing, etc.
Quality	human beautiful clean popular young old new nice pretty soft hard rough smooth, etc.

things, actions, and variabilities with which children are likely to interact.

Labels should be systematically related to a particular category rather than supplied randomly to whatever object, action or variability concept the child happens to be observing. Relating labels to categories will help the child learn, retain, and retrieve a vocabulary much more efficiently. Likewise, *function* words (i.e., words which seem to signal grammatical structure rather than to serve as labels) should be exposed systematically to the child; i.e., they should always be exposed as part of the grammatical configuration of a sentence rather than as isolated labels. Thus the child learns these, not as labels for categories, but rather, as words which help to tie categories together functionally.

Rules for vocabulary *transformations* (for example, man-men, kitty-cat, good-better, etc.) are usually learned by the child implicitly through repeated experience. Experience then serves as not only the vehicle in which concepts and labels are paired, but as the undergirding basis for learning rules of transformations. Thus, the basic vocabulary being taught should be used functionally and correctly by the teacher and children as often as possible in varied situational settings.

Examples of word changes which occur in different conceptual categories are given below.

Number Concepts (plural)	— one car > two cars, etc.	
Time Concepts (tense)	— *present and progressive:*	
	plants > is planting	
	past: plant > planted	
	future: plant > will plant	
Quantity	— *Diminutive*	— cat > kitty
	Comparative	— tall > taller
	Superlative	— tall > tallest
Manner	— *Comparative*	— swift > swifter
	Superlative	— swift > swiftest

Concept categories (and sub-categories) and their respective labels appear to be vulnerable to sensory channels, that is, visual, auditory, and tactile, etc. For example, the concepts of *time* seem to be developed mainly through the auditory channel and are more dependent upon *label* descriptions, while those of *color, size,* and *shape* are almost completely dependent upon experiences through the visual channel; Furth (1964) has shown that visual concepts can be organized with a minimal amount of verbal language. On the other hand, concepts of time depend greatly upon verbal symbols for their acquisition. Thus, in attempts to develop an interaction between classifying and labeling, a certain modality may play a more significant role than others in the learning of the concept, but the auditory modality continuously plays a major role in the labeling of all concepts.

Working with the Basic Sentence. The basic sentence consists of NP + VP (where N = noun, P = phrase, and V = verb). Suppose we have the sentence, "The man carried the book." The first thing we notice is that the verb phrase has been expanded to include another noun phrase. This is a type of sentence modification which children learn early. There are a number of sentences that can be generated from this basic expanded structure through substitution. For example, for "man" might be substituted: boy, child, children, daddy, farmer, friend, girl, lady, men, people, person, woman, etc. For "carried" might be substituted: brought, bought, changed, covered, cut, found, got, gave, has, held, kept, left, lost, moved, opened, ordered, picked, read, received, saw, showed, took, tried, used, etc. For "book" could be substituted any noun word which can serve as the direct object and can be carried by a man. A good procedure in attempting to develop increased language competence in the child is to hold the two "slots" constant while substituting various words into the other slot. Eact time, the statement is given as a whole sentence, however.

Summary. Children perceive concepts as part of experience; concepts are given labels, usually as they are conceived, and the labels come to represent the concepts.

Early concepts of children center around objects, actions, and situations. These concepts change in terms of ways in which objects, actions, and situations vary.

Adjectives and adverbs seem to be the labels most clearly descriptive of variability, that is, of changes in things being perceived. Most of the adjectives and adverbs uttered by a two and a half year old child, for example, can be classified into nine or ten conceptual categories.

The concept categories pertaining to *things, actions,* and *variability* seem to be selectively accessible to sensory channels; for example, the concepts in time category are developed mainly through the auditory channel while those of color and number categories are almost completely visual. Thus, the types of experiences utilized to facilitate language will be partly a function of types of concept labels being worked on. Labels are always paired with experience concepts, either actual or structured, so that they may become part of the concept.

Increasing Motivation by Strengthening Stimulus Variables

The more explicit behavioral modification method of facilitation appears to be at opposite poles to the biological orientation. Variously referred to as "operant conditioning," "behavior modification," etc., in its more formal stage this approach is characterized by rigorous programing of stimulus and reinforcement presentations for the shaping or changing of speech and language patterns (Sloan and MacAulay, 1968). "In this behavioristic . . . approach, there is a relative de-emphasis on assumed processes within the child and more emphasis on what specific educational tasks he needs to be taught" (Bateman, 1967, p. 124). One rationale given for this approach is that diagnosis and etiology lend themselves too easily to constructs which can be manipulated on a verbal level; we therefore seem to know a great deal more about etiology than we do about remediation since remediation bears the burden of having to actually bring about changes on the level of reality. What we need to do, say the behaviorists, is to "see the specific operations they [the children] can perform or not perform and we will deal with these operations [directly]. For us, *that* is diagnosis and knowledge of etiology is relatively useless because we can do very little to manipulate psychosocial factors that breed the behaviors we must confront" (Cohen, 1967, p. 139). One author indicates that "a child's learning and/or development is essentially a complex history of reinforcement contingencies whereby behaviors that exist at one point are gradually shaped into more refined or more complex behaviors through the shifting of existing reinforcement contingencies, or the introduction of new ones. Thus . . . the disability resides, not in the child, but . . . more specifically in the reinforcement contingencies provided by the environment" (Allen, 1967, p. 352).

It is the feeling of the present writer that this apparent polar opposition between related-deficit (i.e., organismic) training and direct-deficit training need not exist. Reinforcement therapy is an approach which increases motivation and systematically strengthens any changes which occur; it really does not matter whether these are changes in organic perceptual skills, or expressive language skills. Reinforcement therapy can greatly increase the efficiency of any kind of training and should be used regularly in all training where increased motivation would help.

We have *traditionally* utilized both a related-deficit and direct-deficit (often referred to as symptomatic) approach in the field of speech pathology and audiology. We have always used some type of reinforcement (both negative and positive) although such reinforcement has usually not been rigorously systematic or programmed and relative strengths or efficiency of reinforcement stimuli being used have not been objectively assessed. As a result, we have used predominantly verbal praise or approval (not a strong reinforcer for some children), or supplied the child with information as to correctness or incorrectness of response. We do not, as a rule, define in a clearcut fashion exactly what the steps or phases of progressive shaping or differential reinforcement will be and leave this too often to intuition during therapy. Number of successes in any phase of therapy often means little to the speech therapist in terms of sustaining of motivation.

A clear example of this latter point is the therapist who indicated that a brain-injured child with whom he was working had very poor memory for colors. "He seems to remember the colors accurately at times and other times he cannot." The therapist indicated that this was probably a symptom of organically fluctuating memory span and possibly some agnosia for color. Observation of the therapy session revealed that the therapist was attempting to get the child to reproduce a rather complex color-block design and to name the colors as he proceded. Further questioning revealed that the task had repeatedly been a difficult one for the child—one which the therapist estimated as being successful in only about one percent of the trials. Needless to say, the child seemed not to be interested when the therapist pointed to blue and said, "Is this red?" and the child automatically and without paying real attention said, "yes."

There are certain cues in therapy which would make one suspect lack of interest or motivation—or even resentment—on the part of the child. If he appears to be attending to the task, but is not. If he is constantly requesting that "we do something else," or that he be permitted to leave. If he reluctantly approaches the task as much as to say, "Oh no! That again!" If he is not *shaping up* or making progress in therapy. These are all cues that his motivation could easily be the result of an inappropriate system of reinforcement, and is often mistaken as an inherent inability to perform a task.

The three most neglected areas in "traditional" therapy are: (1) assessment of strength of reinforcement stimuli; (2) efforts to condition verbal praise as a strong reinforcer, and (3) systematizing successive approximations so as to provide for at least 65% success while at the same time utilizing differential reinforcement within this "minimal success" framework. These three factors are all vital to motivation in therapy. Before reading the discussions which follow, the student who has little or no knowledge about principles of "reinforcement therapy" or "operant conditioning" would do well to turn to the Appendix, which is a condensed review of those principles.

Evaluating the Strength of Reinforcing Stimuli. One can theroretically assess the strength of a reinforcing stimulus (S^r) by plotting the increase in frequency of the response which is presumably reinforced. If the frequency increases rapidly, it could be considered a strong reinforcer. If it increases very slowly, it may be a weak reinforcer. One can readily compare various S^rs as to their relative strengths by using each on a trial basis and plotting the increment curve. The S^r which achieves the steepest slope would be the most effective reinforcer.

Conditioning Verbal Praise as a Strong Reinforcer. Frequently verbal praise (which is the main S^r used in traditional speech therapy) is a weak reinforcer for a child in training. Since the likelihood of generalization (carryover) of this particular S^r into the child's environment is greater than most other S^rs, it is most desirable that verbal praise be strengthened as an S^r. One can do this quite readily by conditioning (pairing) verbal praise with another stronger S^r such as food or tokens. When verbal praise is strongly conditioned,* the stronger reinforcing stimuli can gradually be "faded" out.

Maintaining an Optimal Level of Success in Each Stage of Training. In evaluating the relative percentage of successes necessary to maintain optimal motivation in therapy, one can deliberately vary the number of successes (i.e., responses which will be positively reinforced) upward and downward and notice the resulting drive of the child for sticking to the task and maintaining interest. If drive and interest increases as a result of increasing the successes, then this was a good move. If it decreases, then lack of success experiences may not be the problem. It is recommended that where motivation (or interest) and success experiences are strongly related in a given child, goals for successive approximation should be easy enough as to provide a minimum of 65% success (i.e., 6.5 out of 10 trials successfully performed). This often means lowering the goal of the present task, if the 65% minimal success criterion is not met. Identification of fine increments of shaping, through task analysis, is an important part of planning for therapy.

Strengthening Imitation as a Controlling Stimulus. Imitation can be taught to a non-imitating child by taking the child's hand and putting him passively through the model's motions to be imitated. This is immediately reinforced. Passivity can then gradually be faded as the child becomes more active in imitation. When general imitation (such as arm and hand gesture) is easily obtained from the child, more specific imitations can be initiated.

---

*Resistance to extinction will be greater if a variable-ratio schedule is used throughout the latter part of the conditioning process.

The discriminative cue found by Sloan *et al.* (1968), to be effective was the verbal instruction "do this." More *specific* imitation of oro-facial musculature and associated structures can follow *general* imitative training. "The only difference between this and the previous step is the response selected for imitation. Responses included such things as opening and shutting the mouth, placing the teeth on the lower lip, and different tongue placement . . . . If necessary, 'guidance' of the child's lips, tongue, and mouth was provided when new responses were first introduced" (pp. 79-80). The passive manipulation, if used, can be faded gradually by providing cues to merely suggest the movement desired such as touching the lip for one movement, his chin for another, or holding the thumb and forefinger in a certain way in front of the child when cuing him to open or close the mouth. Even these "cues" are eventually faded so that the child does not remain dependent upon them. Imitation of verbal sounds can become self-reinforcing if this leads to a feeling of more adequate speech production.

An often used short cut for motivating the child to imitate is having him observe the consequences with the model. "First, one might pair a particular model with a number of reinforcers. Thus the child might be directly reinforced by the model or be given extra attention or privileges correlated with the model's presence. Second, the child should observe the model being reinforced for specific responses, perhaps by events which are likely to serve as reinforcers for the child. Hence, the youngster might see the model engaging in verbal behaviors, such as 'Bring me candy,' which are followed by appropriate reinforcement" (Sloan *et al.*, 1968, p. 72).

The use of imitation as a discriminative stimulus (S^d) is called *supportive* S^d (McLean, 1965). The use of stimuli in which imitation plays no part, i.e., use of a picture to be named, is called *evoking* S^d. It is desirable, in teaching vocabulary, for example, to eventually establish an evoking S^d and fade out the supportive S^d. This is due to the fact that most discriminative cues for language productions in one's environment are of an evocative type, e.g., objects, actions, variability, or auditory stimuli.

SUMMARY

This chapter has resulted from an effort to combine linguistic theory and clinical experience to form a frame of reference for facilitating language development in language delayed children. Linguistic theory purports that language is an unfolding process which results from interaction of the maturational propensities within the child and his language stimulating environment. Since biological potential and biologically sensitive age periods play an important role in language development, a sensory-motor developmental point of view is utilized as a supplementary approach in training. Inasmuch as the child reacts to a stimulating environment, almost in the form of a "resonance" reaction, a dynamic environment is structured with which the child has ample opportunity to interact. Since motivation is a most important single determinant of progress in training, "reinforcement therapy" principles are utilized in all phases of training where motivation needs to be increased. Imitation apparently plays an important role in the initial phase of the language behavior of the child; thus, suggestions are offered for use of imitation in achieving more rapid approximations of the teacher's model expressions.

REFERENCES

ALLEN, K. E.: The strengthening of adjustive behaviors through systematic application of reinforcement procedures. In *Proceedings of the 1967 International Convocation on Children and Young Adults with Learning Disabilities.* Home for Crippled Children, Pittsburg, Pa., 1967; pp. 351-371.

AYRES, J.: Remedial procedures based on neurobehavioral constructs. In *Proceedings of the 1967 International Convocation on Children and Young Adults with Learning Disabilities.* Home for Crippled Children, Pittsburg, Pa., 1967; pp. 203-206.

BANGS, T. E.: *Language and Learning Disorders of the Pre-Academic Child.* New York, Appleton-Century-Crofts, 1968.

BATEMAN, B.: Three approaches to diagnosis and educational planning for children with learning disabilities. In *Proceedings of the 1967*

International Convocation on Children and Young Adults with Learning Disabilities. Home for Crippled Children, Pittsburg, Pa., 1967:pp. 120-129.

BEASLEY, J.: *Slow to Talk.* New York, Columbia University Teachers College, Bureau of Publications, 1956.

BOBATH, K., and BOBATH, B.: The facilitation of normal postural reactions and movements in the treatment of cerebral palsy. *Physiotherapy, 50*:245-262, 1964.

COHEN, S. A.: Diagnosis and etiology or operation overthink. In *Proceedings of the 1967 International Convocation on Children and Young Adults with Learning Disabilities.* Home for Crippled Children, Pittsburg, Pa., 1967; pp. 135-142.

DELACATO, C. H.: *Neurological Organization and Reading.* Springfield, Ill., Charles C. Thomas, 1966.

FROSTIG, M.: Training in sensory-motor functions. In *Proceedings of the 1967 International Convocation on Children and Young Adults with Learning Disabilities.* Home for Crippled Children, Pittsburg, Pa., 1967; pp. 170-183.

FROSTIG, M., and HORNE, B. A.: *The Frostig Program for the Development of Visual Perception.* Chicago, Follett Publishing Co., 1964.

FURTH, H. G.: *Thinking without Language.* New York, Free Press, 1966.

IRWIN, O. C., and HAMMIL, D. D.: An abstraction test for use with cerebral palsied children, *Cerebral Palsy Review, 24*:3-9, 1964.

KEPHART, N. C.: *The Slow Learner in the Classroom.* Columbus, Ohio, C. E. Merrill Books, 1960.

KEPHART, N. C.: The needs of teachers in specialized information on perception. In CRUICKSHANK, W. M. (Ed.): *The Teacher of Brain-injured Children.* New York, Syracuse University Press, 1966.

LENNEBERG, E. H.: *The Biological Basis of Language.* New York, Wiley, 1967.

LENNEBERG, E. H.: The natural history of language. In SMITH, F., and MILLER, G. A. (Eds.): *The Genesis of Language.* Cambridge, The M.I.T. Press, 1966.

LOW, G. M., Curriculum guide for Training Aids. Provo, Utah, BYU Speech Clinic, 1969.

McDONALD, E. T., and AUNGST, L. F.: Studies in oral sensorimotor function. In BOSMA, J. F.: *Symposium on Oral Sensation and Perception.* Springfield, Ill., Charles C. Thomas, 1967.

McLEAN, J. E.: Shifting stimulus control of articulatory responses by operant techniques. University of Kansas, Unpublished doctoral dissertation, 1965.

MECHAM, M. J.: *Vebral Language Development Scale.* Minneapolis, Minn., American Guidance Service, 1959.

MECHAM, M. J., et al.: Utah Test of Language Development. Salt Lake City, Communication Research Associates, 1967.

MOULTON, W. G.: *A Linguistic Guide to Language Learning.* New York, Modern Language Association of America, 1966.

ROOD, M. S.: Neurophysiological reactions as a basis for physical therapy. *Physiotherapy Review, 34*:444, 1954.

SHANNON, C. E., and WEAVER, W.: *The Mathematical Theory of Communication.* Urbana, University of Illinois Press, 1949, as reported by STANILAND, A. C.: *Patterns of Redundancy.* Cambridge, Univ. Press, 1966, p. 43.

SHELTON, R. L., Jr., *et al.*: Testing oral stereognosis. In BOSMA, J. F. (Ed.): *Symposium on Oral Sensation and Perception.* Springfield, Ill., Charles C. Thomas, 1967.

SLOAN, H. N., Jr., and MacAULAY, B. D. (Eds.): *Operant Procedures in Remedial Speech and Language Training.* Boston, Haughton Mifflin Co., 1968.

STANILAND, A. C.: *Patterns of Redundancy.* Cambridge, University Press, 1966.

VYGOTSKY, L.: Thought and Language (Translated by E. HAVEMANN and G. VKAR). Cambirdge, M.I.T. Press, 1962.

WEIR, R. H.: *Language in the Crib.* The Hague, Mouton and Company, 1962.

WOODRUFF, A. D.: *Basic Concepts of Teaching.* San Franciso, Chandler Publishing Co., 1961.

OUTLINE OF THE MAIN
ELEMENTS OF OPERANT CONDITIONING

Following is a brief outline of the main elements of operant conditioning. For a more extended study or review of operant conditioning principles, the reader is encouraged to seek out more extended sources. The present author recommends that the beginning student refer to one of two small books on operant conditioning which give simplified descriptions and offer extended references to more complex discourses: (1) SMITH, W. I., and MOORE, J. W.: *Conditioning and Instrumental Learning.* New York, McGraw-Hill Book Company, 1966; and (2) REYNOLDS, G. S.: *A Primer of Operant Conditioning.* New York, Scott, Foresman and Company, 1968.

OPERANT CONDITIONING

A process by which a behavior's frequency of occurrence is modified by its consequences.

STIMULUS

Any element of the environment which can excite any of the organisms' sensory receptors may serve as a stimulus.

RESPONSE

Any segment of an organism's behavior or motor activity.

REINFORCEMENT

Reinforcement is a stimulus event occuring as a consequence of a behavior, which serves to increase the frequency of that same behavior. If the reinforcing event happens to be the appearance or beginning of a stimulus, the stimulus is called a *positive* reinforcer. If the reinforcing event happens to be the disappearance or cessation of a stimulus, the stimulus is called a *negative* reinforcer. Negative reinforcement occurs as a result of removal of noxious stimulation and positive reinforcement occurs as a result of presentation of desired stimulation.

REINFORCING STIMULI

Primary (or unconditioned) *reinforcers,* such as food and water, can reinforce behavior without any previous experience in relationship to them. *Secondary* (or conditioned) *reinforcers* acquire power to reinforce only by frequently being paired with primary reinforcers.

CONTROLLING OR DISCRIMINATIVE STIMULI

A stimulus, whose presence cues the organism that reinforcement will likely follow a behavior and whose absence cues the organism that reinforcement will not take place, is called a controlling or discriminative stimulus.

CONDITIONING

Conditioning is a circumstance in which either behavior is being strengthened or increased by its consequences or a stimulus is acquiring controlling or reinforcing value by being paired with another primary or conditioned stimulus.

GENERALIZATION

Generalization is a phenomenon in which an unconditioned stimulus, because of its similarity to a conditioned stimulus, will evoke the same response or serve in the same rewarding way as a conditioned stimulus.

EXTINCTION

Reduction of the frequency of a conditioned behavior because reinforcement is no longer present is called behavioral extinction.

DIFFERENTIAL REINFORCEMENT

When certain response variants are reinforced and others are not, this phenomena is called differential reinforcement.

SUCCESSIVE APPROXIMATION

When we change criteria or goals by which we determine which responses will be differentially reinforced, this is called successive approximation.

SHAPING OR PROGRESSION

Shaping or progression is the use of both differential reinforcement and successive approximation coordinately.

AUTHOR INDEX

A

Allen, K. E., 61, 65
Ames, L., 33, 41
Aungst, L. F., 42, 66
Ayres, A. J., 12, 20, 40, 44, 46, 65

B

Bangs, T. E., 38, 41, 54, 65
Bateman, B., 60, 65
Beasley, J., 52, 66
Bellugi, U., 11, 40, 41, 42
Berko, F. G., 21, 42
Berko, J., 39, 40
Berko, M. J., 21, 42
Bernstein, B., 38, 40
Blum, L. H., 41
Bobath, B., 46, 66
Bobath, K., 46, 66
Bosma, J. F., 35, 42, 66
Braine, M. D. S., 40, 41
Brown, R., 11, 25, 30, 40, 41, 42
Burgemeister, B., 33, 41

C

Carroll, J. B., 25, 26, 38, 30
Carrow, M. A., Sr., 39, 41
Cattell, R. B., 33, 41
Chomsky, N., 29, 30, 38, 41
Cohen, S. A., 60, 66
Copeland, R. H., 31
Crabtree, M., 41
Crickmay, M. C., 13, 14, 20
Cruickshank, W. M., 66

D

Davis, E. A., 41
Darley, F. L., 37, 41
Delacato, C. H., 46, 66

Dumbleton, C., 43
Dunn, L. J., 34, 37, 41

E

Erikson, E. H., 23, 30
Ervin, S., 11, 28, 31, 40, 42

F

Fisher, M. S., 37, 41
Foss, B. M., 31
Fraser, C., 25, 30, 41
Frostig, M., 46, 66
Fry, D. B., 27, 30
Furth, H., 66

G

Galanter, E., 16, 21
Gesell, A., 12, 21
Gleason, H. A., 10, 11
Goodenough, F. L., 33, 41
Griffith, D. L., 37, 41

H

Halle, M., 25, 30
Hammil, D. D., 34, 41, 66
Hardy, W. G., 19, 21
Holland, J. G., 28, 30
Horne, B. A., 66
Hymes, D., 41

I

Ilg, F., 41
Ingalls, S. I., 37, 41
Irwin, O. C., 28, 31, 34, 35, 41, 66

J

Jacobs, R. A., 10, 11
Jakobson, R., 25, 30

71

Jensen, P. J., 35, 41
Jex, J. L., 11, 34, 42
Jones, J. D., 11, 42

K

Kephart, N. C., 3, 11, 21, 43, 46, 61, 66
Kirk, S. A., 40, 41
Kirk, W. D., 40, 41
Kohler, R., 35, 41

L

Lee, L., 40, 42
Leiter, R. G., 33, 42
Lenneberg, E. H., 2, 3, 11, 12, 18, 19,
   20, 21, 25, 31, 35, 42, 45, 54, 66
Levin, H., 31
Lieberman, P., 16, 21
Low, G. M., 54, 66
Luria, A. R., 12, 19, 21, 31
Lynn, R., 19, 21

Mc

McCarthy, D., 37, 42
McCarthy, J. J., 40, 41
McDonald, E. T., 35, 42, 50, 66
McLean, J. E., 66
McNeill, D., 3, 11

M

MacAulay, B. D., 31, 60, 67
Mandler, G., 6, 29, 30, 31
Mark, H. J., 19, 21
Mecham, M. J., 8, 11, 21, 34, 36, 37,
   42, 66
Menyuk, P., 40, 42
Miller, G. A., 25, 31, 26, 28, 29, 42, 66
Miller, W., 11
Moll, K. L., 37, 41
Montessori, M., 26
Moore, J. W., 68
Moulton, W. G., 2, 9, 10, 11, 18, 21, 27,
   31, 51, 67
Musgrave, B. S., 30
Mussen, P., 23, 24, 27, 31
Mysak, E. D., 13, 14, 21, 42, 47

N

Newcomb, T., 31
Nice, M. M., 37, 42

O

Olds, J., 28, 31
Olds, M., 28, 31

P

Palmer, M. J., 21
Penfield, W., 35, 43
Pronovost, W., 43

R

Reynolds, G. S., 68
Roach, E. G., 43
Roberts, L., 35, 43
Rood, M. S., 46, 67
Rosenbaum, P. S., 10, 11

S

Schiefelbusch, R. L., 22, 23, 31
Sears, R. R., 31
Shaefer, R. B., 24, 31
Shannon, C. E., 51, 67
Shelton, R. L., 67
Shriner, T. H., 37, 43
Skinner, B. F., 28, 30
Sloan, H. N., Jr., 24, 27, 31, 60, 64, 67
Smith, F., 28, 31, 42, 66
Smith, J. O., 31
Smith, M. E., 37, 43
Smith, W. I., 68
Staniland, A. C., 51, 67

T

Taylor, M., 4, 11
Templin, M. C., 37, 43

V

Van Riper, C., 27, 31
Vygotsky, L., 54, 67

W

Weaver, W., 51, 67
Weir, R. H., 40, 43, 67
Wepman, J. M., 4, 11, 43
Winitz, H., 43
Winterbottom, M. R., 28, 31
Woodruff, A. D., 52, 67

SUBJECT INDEX

A

Abstracting, 15, 18, 19
Academic skills, 3
Accent, 27
Activation syndrome, 29
Age, 19, 22
Age *vs.* maturation, 36
Age of onset, 36
Aggressiveness, 24
Analogies, 26
Analysis of language structure, 38
Approximations, 25
Articulation, 15, 16, 17
Attachment, 23, 24
Attention, 22
Audiolinguistic development
  stages of, 44
Audiolinguistic ladder, 35, 36
Audiolinguistic tests, 32
Audiolinguistics
  definition, v
  developmental, v
  disorders of, v
  skills of, v, 22
Audiolinguists, 5
Auditory channel, 15
Auditory channel and labeling, 59
Auditory perception, 47
Auditory training, 47, 48, 49

B

Behavior modification, 60
Behavioral competence, 47
Behavioral milestones, 3
Behavioral performance, 47

Bilateral orientation, 13, 14
Bilateral synchrony, 13
Biting reflex, 14
Boston University Discrimination test, 34
Brain levels, 12
Breathing, 15

C

Categories,
  labels for, 26
Categorization, 16, 18, 25
Cerebrum, 13, 20
Chewing reflex, 14
Classification, 26
Cognition, 15
Communication
  imitation of, 25
Concept labels, 19
Concepts, 59
  action, 26
Conceptual relationships
  organization of, 25
Concrete concepts, 19
Conditioning, 22, 69
Conscience, 24
Content words, 8
Contextual clues, 16
Contrived experiences, 52, 53, 54
Controlling stimulus, 69
Cortex, 13
Crawling, 24
Creativity, 28
Critical period, 20
Cultures
  primitive, 2

D

Decoding, 18
Demonstrations, 54
Dependency, 23
Detection, 15, 16
Developmental experiences, 3
Developmental ladder, 38
Developmental sequences, 3
Developmental tests, 36
Dexterity, 14
Dialect, 27
Differential reinforcement, 25, 70
Direct deficit approach, 61
Direct experience, 53
Discrimination, 15, 16, 17
Discriminative stimulus, 69
Distractibility, 24
Dramatized experiences, 54

E

Early development, 5
Early experiences, 55
Early stimulation, 22
Encoding, 18
Environment, 22, 25
Equilibrium reactions, 14
Equilibrium systems, 13
Experience
  aversive, 29
  opportunities, 25
  repertoire, 15
  varieties of, 4
Experiential enrichment, 52
Extensor tonus, 13
External model, 28
Extinction, 70

F

Facial response, 14
Fear, 29
Field trips, 54
Figure-ground, 16
Function words, 8, 58

G

Generalization, 69
Generative rules, 26
Generative theory, 29
Goodenough Draw-a-Man test, 33

Grammatical decoding, 4, 5, 8
Grammatical encoding, 4, 5, 8
Grammatical structure, 8

H

Haptic-kinesthetic channel, 15
Headstart teachers, v
Houston Test for Language
  Development, 37
Hyperactivity, 24

I

Identification, 24
Imitation, 24, 25, 27
  strengthening, 63, 64
Implicit learning, 29
Impoverished social input, 45
Imprinting, 19
Incomplete man test, 33
Independence, 28
Information integration, 4
Inhibition, 13, 14

J

jnd, 16

L

Labeling and vocabulary development, 54
Labels
  supplying, 54
Labels for categories, 25, 58
Landou reflex, 13
Language
  acquisition, 18
  age progressions, 8
  biological readiness for, 45
  channels, 15
  developmental dimension, 3
  elaborateness, 40
  facilitation of, vi
  forms compared, 2
  history of, 2
  in education, 2
  in illiterate populations, 2
  landmarks, 8
  measurement, 3
  milestones of, 5
  modes of, 2
  onset of, 3

processes of, 4
restrictedness, 40
semantic, 27
sequencing, 12
storage, 12
unfolding of, 3
unfolding process in, 45
Language competence, 38
Language development,
 innate propensities for, 45
Language and experience, 52
Language exposure, 25
Language learning, 26
Language and learning
 assessment test, 38
Language performance, 38, 39, 40
Laterality, 14
Lateralization, 20
Learning
 emotional climate for, 52
 implicit, 28
Learning heirarchies, 3
Leiter I. P. Scale, 33
Length of verbal expressions, 37
Linguistic structure, 8
Linguistic texts, 10
Listening, 2

M

Maturation, 3
Maturational stages, 51
Mimicry, 27
Memory, 25
 long term, 18
 short term, 18
Model, 25
 copy of, 24
 listening to, 53
 nuturant, 24
 presence of, 53
Monitoring, 18, 27
Moral behavior, 24
Moro reflex, 13
Morphological changes, 58
Mother as stimulator, 23
Mothers,
 non-nuturant, 24

N

Neurobehavioral philosophy, 12
New conceptions
 creation of, 29

O

Operant conditioning, 60, 68
Oral-cephalic reflexes, 13
Oral stereognosis, 47
Oral stereognostic training, 49, 50
Organism
 strengthening of, 46
Organization of categories, 26
Organizational plasticity, 20
Oroneuromotor behavior, 14

P

Perception, 15
Perceptual-motor appraisal, 51
Perceptual-motor match, 21
Perceptual-motor system, 12
Phonation, 15
Phonological encoding, 4
Phonemes, 2
Postural systems, 13
Pouting, 14
Practice, 27
PPVT, 34, 37
Premature experience, 45
Programming, 29
Progress in therapy, 62
Progression, 70

Q

Quantitative evaluation, 5
Question words, 9

R

Rate of emergence, 36
Reading, 2
Readiness stages, 3
Reality
 experience with, 25
Recall, 15
Recognition, 15, 16
Redundancies, 4
Reinforcement, 61, 62
 definition, 69
 generalization, 28

negative, 23, 29
positive, 23, 29
Reinforcement therapy, 60
Reinforcing stimuli, 61, 69
Rejection, 15
Related deficit approach, 61
Remedial Center for Communication
    Disorders, vi
Resentment in therapy, 62
Resonance theory of language
    development, 45
Response
    definition, 68
Response variations, 3, 4
Reward, 28
Righting reflexes, 13, 14
Rooting reactions, 14
Rules, 26, 29
    storage of, 18

S

Scanning, 15, 18
Schizophrenia, 23
Segmental drill, 53
Self-control, 24
Self-dependency, 24
Semantic decoding, 4, 5, 8
Semantic encoding, 4, 5, 8
Semantic function, 3
Sense organs, v
Sensitivity, 19, 20
Sensory channels and concepts, 58
Sensory data
    generalization of, 3
    integration of, 4
Sensory experiences, 53
Sensory modes, 26
Sensory-motor deficits, 46
Sentence
    complex, 9
    compound, 9
    contracted, 9
    definition of, 9
    elliptical, 9
    expanded, 9
    parts, 9
Sentence training, 59
Shaping, 70

Social responsiveness, 22, 23
Spatial distance, 24
Spatial exploration, 24
Speaking in man, 2
Speech
    onset of, 3
Speech therapist, v
Spontaneity, 26
Standardized tests, 8, 32
Standards for tests, 32
Stanford-Binet, 35
Stimulus
    definition, 68
Stimulus recall, 18
Stimulus variable, 60
Strengthening the environment, 50 ff
Sub-categories, 26
Success
    optimal, 63
Success experience, 61
Successive approximations, 27, 62, 70
Suckling reflex, 14
Supportive stimuli, 64
Symbiotic psychosis, 24
Symbolic processes, 8
Syntactic function, 3

T

Template, 25
Templin discrimination tests, 35
Testing ability to abstract, 33
Testing ability to form concepts, 33
Testing auditory discrimination, 34
Testing auditory identification, 34
Testing auditory memory, 35
Testing instruments, 32
Testing listening accuracy, 34
Testing morphology, 39
Testing oral stereognosis, 35
Testing perceptual functions, 32
Testing related deficits, 32
Testing syntax, 39
Therapy
    developmental frame of reference
        for, 45
    sensative age for, 45
Tonicity reflexes, 13
Transformations, 29, 58

adjectival clause, 10
adverbial clause, 10
command, 9
coordinate, 9
negative, 9
nominal clause, 18
order, 9
passive, 9
question, 9
substitute, 9
Transformational rules, 58
Triggering, 51
Triggering mechanism for language, 30

U

Universal milestones, 3
Utah Test of Language
  Development, 3, 7, 8
  norms for, 8

V

Variability, 26
  adjectives and adverbs as labels for, 59
Verbal Language Development Scale, 36
Verbal praise, 61, 62, 63
Vineland Social Maturity Scale, 37
Voiced phonemes, 18
Voiceless phonemes, 18

W

Walking, 24
Wepman Discrimination test, 34
Winterhaven Lions, 46
WISC, 35
Word classes
  closed, 8
  open, 8
Word parts, 8
Writing, 2